THE GOOD CHILD'S REWARD.

Train up a Child in the way he should go & when he is old he will not depart from it.

Flowers of Delight

Flowers of Delight

culled by

LEONARD DE VRIES

from the Osborne Collection
of Early Children's Books

*An agreeable Garland of Prose and Poetry
for the Instruction and Amusement
of little Masters and Misses
and their distinguished Parents*

Embellished with some 700 elegant Woodcuts and Engravings on
Wood and Copper of which upwards of 125 are neatly coloured

Selected with the greatest Care from
Books for juvenile Minds
1765 – 1830

Designed by Eric Ayers

PANTHEON BOOKS

Contents

5

Dedicated to

Judith St. John

and

Edgar Osborne

The Children
in the Wood

A great many years ago there lived in the county of Norfolk a gentleman and his lady. The gentleman was brave, kind, and of a noble spirit; and the lady was gentle, beautiful, and virtuous. They were very much loved by all who knew them; for they were always trying to do service to every body who came near them, or who had any thing at all to do with them.

This lady and gentleman lived together very happily for many years, for they loved each other most tenderly. They had two children, who were as yet very young; for the eldest, who was a boy, was but three years old, and the youngest, who was a girl, not quite two years old. The boy was very much like his father, and the girl was like her mother.

By the end of this time the gentleman fell sick, and day after day he grew worse. His lady, as I have just said, loved him with the greatest fondness; and she was so much grieved by his illness that she fell sick too. No physic, nor any thing else, was of the least use to them, for their illness got worse and worse; and they saw that they should soon be taken away from their two little babies, and be forced to leave them in the world without a father or mother.

They bore this cruel thought as well as they could; and trusted, that after they were dead, their children would find some kind friend or another to bring them up. They talked to one another tenderly about them, and at last agreed to send for the gentleman's brother, and give their darlings into his care.

As soon as ever the gentleman's brother heard this news he made all the haste he could to the bed-side where the father and mother were lying sick.

" Ah ! brother," said the dying man, " you see how short a time I can expect to live; yet neither death, nor pain, can give me half so much grief as I feel at the thought of what these dear babes will do without a parent's care. Brother, brother," said the gentleman, putting out his hand as well as he could, and pointing to the children, " they will have none but you to be kind to them; none but you to see them clothed and fed, and teach them to be good and happy."

" Dear, dear brother," said the dying lady, " you must be father, mother, and uncle, too, to these lovely little lambs. First let William be taught to read; and then he should be told how good his father was. And little Jane,—Oh ! brother, it wrings my heart to talk of her: think of the gentle usage she will stand in need of, and take her fondly on your knee, brother, and she and William too will repay your care with love."

The uncle then answered, " Oh ! how it grieves my heart to see you, my dearest brother and sister, in this sad state ! but take comfort, there may still be hope of your getting well: yet if we should happen to lose you, I will do all you can desire for your darling children. In me they shall find a father, mother, and uncle. William shall learn to read; and shall be often told how good his father was, that he may turn out as good himself when he grows up to be a man. Jane shall be used with the most tender care, and shall be kindly fondled on my knee. But, dear brother, you have said nothing of the riches you must leave behind. I am sure you know my heart too well

9

to think that I speak of this for any other reason than your dear children's good, and that I may be able to make use of all your money only for their sake."

"Pray, brother," said the dying man, "do not grieve me with talking of any such thing; for how could you, who will be their father, mother, and uncle too, once think of wronging them? Here, here, brother, is my will. You will see how I have done the best I could for my babes."

A few moments after the gentleman had said these words, he pressed his cold lips to the children; the lady did the same, and in a short time they both died.

The uncle shed a few tears at this sad sight, and then broke open the will; in which he found that his brother had left the little boy, William, the sum of three hundred pounds a year, when he should be twenty-one years old, and to Jane, the girl, the sum of five hundred pounds in gold, to be paid her the day of her being married. But if the children should happen to die before coming of age, then all the money was to belong to their uncle. The will of the gentleman next ordered

that he and his dear wife should be buried side by side in the same grave.

The two little children were now taken home to the house of their uncle; who, for some time, did just as their parents had so lately told him upon their death-bed; and so he used them with great kindness. But when he had kept them about a year, he forgot by degrees to think how their father and mother looked when they gave their children to his care, and how he himself had made a promise to be their father, mother, and uncle, all in one.

After a little more time had passed; the uncle could not help thinking that he wished the little boy and girl would die, for then he should have all their money for himself; and when he had once begun to think this, he went on till he could hardly think of any thing else. At last he said to himself: "It would not be very hard for me to kill them so as for nobody to know any thing at all about the matter, and then the money will be mine at once."

When the cruel uncle had once brought his mind to kill the helpless little creatures, he was not long in finding a way to bring it about. He hired two sturdy ruffians, who had already killed many travellers in a dark thick wood, some way off, for the sake of robbing them of their money. These two wicked creatures now agreed with the uncle, for a large sum of money, to do the most cruel deed that ever yet was heard of; and so the uncle began to get every thing ready for them.

He told an artful story to his wife, of what good it would do to the children to put them forward in their learning; and how he had a friend in London who would take great care of them. He then said to the poor little things: "Should not you like, my pretty ones, to see the famous town of London; where you, William, can buy a fine wooden horse to ride upon all day long, and a whip to make him gallop, and a fine sword to wear by your side? And you, Jane, shall have pretty frocks, and pretty dolls, and many other pretty play things; and a nice gilded coach shall be got to take you there."

"Oh yes, I will go, uncle," said William: "Oh yes, I will go, uncle," said Jane: and the uncle, with a heart as hard as stone, soon got them ready for the journey.

The harmless little creatures were put into a

At last the two ruffians fell into such a great passion about killing the poor babes, that the one who wished to spare their lives took out the great knife he had brought to murder them and stabbed the other to the heart, so that he fell down dead at his feet.

The one who had killed him was now at a loss what to do with the children; for he wanted to get away as fast as he could for fear of being found in the wood. At last he thought the only thing he could do was, to leave them in the wood by themselves, and trust them to the kindness of any body that might happen to pass by and find them there.

" Come here, my pretty ones," said he, " you must take hold of my hands and go a little way along with me." The poor children took each a hand, and went on; but the tears burst from their eyes, and their little limbs shook with fear all the while.

In this way he led them for about two miles further on in the wood; and then told them to wait there till he came back from the next town, where he would go and get them some food.

fine coach a few days after; and along with them the two cruel wretches, who were soon to put an end to their merry prattle, and turn their smiles into tears. One of them drove the coach, and the other sat inside between little William and little Jane.

When they had reached the entrance of the dark thick wood, the two ruffians took them out of the coach, telling them they might now walk a little way and gather some flowers; and while the children were skipping about like lambs, the ruffians turned their backs to them and began to talk about what they had to do.

" In good truth," said the one who had been sitting between the children all the way, " now I have seen their sweet faces, and heard that pretty talk, I have no heart to do the cruel deed: let us fling away the ugly knife, and send the children back to their uncle." " But indeed I will not," said the other: " what is their pretty talk to us ? And who will pay us for being so tender hearted ?" " Think of your own children at home," answered the first. " Yes, but I shall get nothing to take back to them, if I turn coward as you would have me to do," replied the other.

In the mean time the wicked uncle thought they had been killed as he ordered, so he told all the folks who asked him about them, an artful tale of their having died in London of the small-pox; and he then took all their fortune to himself, and lived upon it as if it had been his own by good right.

But all this did him very little service; for soon after his wife died; and as he could not help being very unhappy, and was always thinking too that he saw the bleeding children before his eyes, he did not attend at all to his affairs; so that, instead of growing richer, he grew poorer every day. Besides this his two sons had gone on board a ship to try their fortune abroad, but they both were drowned at sea, and he became quite wretched, so that his life was a burden to him.

When things had gone on in this manner for some years, the ruffian, who took pity on the children and would not kill them, robbed some person in that very wood; and being pursued, he was laid hold of and brought to prison, and soon after was tried before a judge and was found guilty: so that he was condemned to be hanged for the crime.

As soon as he found that his death must be, he sent for the keeper of the prison, and owned to him all the crimes he had been guilty of in his whole life. Thus he made known the story of the two children; and, at the same time, told that part of the wood he had left them to starve in.

The news of this matter soon reached the wicked uncle's ears; who was already broken-hearted for the many ills that had happened to himself, and could not bear the load of public shame that he knew must now fall upon him, so he lay down upon his bed, and died that very day.

As soon as ever the tidings of the death of the two children were made public, proper persòns were sent to search the wood for them; and, after a great deal of trouble, the pretty babes were at last found stretched in each other's arms; with William's arm round the neck of Jane, his face turned close to hers, and his frock pulled over her body. They were quite covered over with leaves, which in all that time had never withered; and on a bush near this cold grave, there sat a robin red-breast watching and chirping; so that many gentle hearts still think it was this kind bird that did bring the leaves and cover the little babes over with them.

William took his sister Jane by the hand, and they walked in fear up and down the wood. " Will the strange man come with some cakes, Billy ? " said little Jane. " By and by, dear Jane," said William: And soon after, " I wish I had some cakes, Billy," said she. They then looked about with their little eyes to every part of the wood; and it would have melted a heart as hard as stone, to see how sad they looked, and how they listened to every sound of wind in the trees.

After they had waited a very long time, they tried to fill their bellies with blackberries: but they soon ate all that were within their reach. Night was now coming on; and William, who had tried all he could to comfort his little sister, at last wanted comfort himself: so when Jane said once more, " How hungry I am, Billy, I b-e-l-ieve —I cannot help crying— " William burst out a-crying too; and down they lay upon the cold earth; and pulling their arms round each others neck, there they starved, and there they died.

Thus were these two pretty harmless babes murdered; and as no one knew of their death, so there was no one to dig a grave and bury them.

The Parlour Teacher

LET us save the crumbs as they fall from the loaf when the bread is cut, then we can put them in a plate, and set it at our win-dow next the gar-den; and we may see the birds come and eat them. It is bet-ter to save the crumbs of bread thus, than to throw them in-to the fire.

When Jane had cut the rind from off her cheese, she did not throw it a-way; but she took her knife and cut it up in-to small bits, then put some crumbs of bread to it, and laid them on the gar-den wall; so e-ve-ry day, in win-ter, there came a lit-tle red-breast to eat them, and in re-turn he would sit on a tree, just by the house, and sing a sweet song.

At a vil-lage near Lon-don, there did live a poor gar-den-er, who had ma-ny chil-dren, one of whom fell ill of the small-pox, and all the rest of the lit-tle ones caught it. Their mo-ther al-so fell ill with the dis-ease, and di-ed. Poor lit-tle babes they cri-ed sad-ly; but some kind wo-men, who were not rich, went to the help of the poor babes, and they all got well a-gain.

The doc-tor of the vil-lage then sent for all the poor chil-dren, and all the poor men and wo-men, who had not had the small-pox, and i-no-cu-lat-ed them with the cow-pox, for he had found out, that who-e-ver had once had that dis-ease, ne-ver had the small-pox; and by this kind act he sav-ed much pain and trou-ble, if not ma-ny va-lu-a-ble lives.

STORIES
of
INSTRUCTION
and
DELIGHT

L O N D O N

Printed and Sold by
John Marshall
Nº 4. Aldermary Church Yard
in Bow Lane Cheapside.

The CAMEL.

MR. Wilson having business that called him from home, one morning gave each of his sons a lesson to learn in his absence. Soon after he was gone some men with a camel and a monkey stopped opposite to the house. When the man began to play the taber and pipe both the boys flew to the window to see what was in the street. William staid a few minutes just to observe the camel and then returned to his studies, but Robert was so diverted with the tricks of the monkey that he forgot the time, and it was not long before his papa returned that he left the window. Robert not being able to say his lesson was punished, but William, who had been a good boy and learnt his lesson, was rewarded.

The BALLOON.

MR. Herbert had a house and garden a short distance from London, to which he used to retire every day after the hours of business. One afternoon, when a balloon was expected to ascend, he left town earlier than usual, to enjoy with his family the sight of this curious contrivance. Little Mary, Charles, and his eldest son Henry, were already in the garden, eagerly expecting to see it floating in the air. Soon after Mr. and Mrs. Herbert joined the little party the balloon began to ascend, and, to their great surprise, they clearly distinguished, with the telescope, two gentlemen and a lady seated in the car. The balloon moved gently forward, and afforded the young folk much pleasure.

LAUNCHING of a SHIP.

WILLIAM was a good boy, he always paid proper attention to his lessons, and did every thing that his papa bid him. He had heard that a ship was to be launched, and wished very much to see it, but his papa was fearful of any accident happening to him in consequence of the crowd. His papa, however, recollected that a friend lived near the place where he knew they would be welcome.

William and his papa hastened there, and he was placed at a window, from whence he had an uninterrupted view of this pleasing sight.

The BALLOON ROUND-ABOUT.

MR. and Mrs. Wilson, with little Henry, went to take a walk in the fair. In one part they observed a new contrivance, the ingenuity of which they could not help admiring, and little Henry was so much delighted with it that they could scarcely pacify him, he begged over and over again to have a ride with the little boys and girls, but when his papa and mamma told him that it was a dangerous amusement, and not proper for him, he persisted no longer in his entreaties, but went quietly with them to view some other part of the fair.

The PARACHUTES.

LITTLE Tommy Playful and his brother were boys of good dispositions, but so very idle that it was difficult to make them learn any thing, and they were likewise so fickle in their amusements that the whole house was crammed with the toys that had been discarded. It was now the rage for balloons and parachutes, and there was no rest till little Tommy and his brother had one too. Every thing for a time was neglected for this new toy, but it soon like the rest fell into disrepute, and made part of the lumber that lay littering in every part of the house.

SELECT RHYMES

FOR THE

NURSERY,

WITH COPPERPLATE ENGRAVINGS

London:

PRINTED BY AND FOR DARTON AND HARVEY

Gracechurch-Street.

——

1808.

[Price One Shilling.]

THE COW.

THANK you, pretty cow, that made
Pleasant milk, to soak my bread;
Ev'ry day, and ev'ry night,
Warm, and fresh, and sweet, and white.

Do not chew the hemlock rank,
Growing on the weedy bank;
But the yellow cowslips eat,
They will make it very sweet.

Where the purple violet grows,
Where the bubbling water flows,
Where the grass is fresh and fine,
Pretty cow, go there and dine.

LEARNING TO GO ALONE.

COME, my darling, come away,
Take a pretty walk to day;
Run along, and never fear,
I'll take care of baby dear;
Up and down with little feet,
That's the way to walk, my sweet.
Now it is so very near,
Soon she'll get to mother dear:
There she comes along at last,
Here's my finger, hold it fast;
Now one pretty little kiss,
After such a walk as this.

GOING TO BED.

DOWN upon my pillow warm,
  I do lay my little head,
And the rain, and wind, and storm,
  Cannot come a-nigh my bed.

Many little children poor,
  Have not any where to go,
And sad hardships they endure,
  Such as I did never know.

Dear mamma, I'll thank you oft,
  For this comfortable bed,
And this pretty pillow soft,
  Where I rest my little head.

I shall sleep till morning light,
  On a bed so nice as this,
So, my dear mamma, good night,
  Give your little girl a kiss.

THE LITTLE GIRL THAT BEAT HER SISTER.

Go, go, my naughty girl, and kiss
  Your little sister dear;
I must not have such things as this,
  Nor noisy quarrels here.

What ! little children scold and fight,
  That ought to be so mild !
O ! Mary, 'tis a shocking sight
  To see an angry child.

I can't imagine, for my part,
  The reason of your folly;
As if she did you any hurt,
  By playing with your dolly !

See, how the little tears do run
  Fast, from her wat'ry eye;
Come, my sweet innocent, have done,
  'Twill do no good to cry.

Go, Mary, wipe her tears away,
  And make it up with kisses,
And never turn a pretty play
  To such a pet as this is.

NO BREAKFAST FOR GROWLER.

No, naughty Growler, get away,
  You shall not have a bit;
Now, when I speak, how dare you stay !
I can't spare any, Sir, I say,
  And so you need not sit.

Poor Growler ! do not make him go,
  But recollect, before,
That he has never serv'd you so,
For you have given him many a blow,
  That patiently he bore.

Poor Growler ! if he could but speak,
  He'd tell, (as well he might,)
How he would bear with many a freak,
And wag his tail and look so meek,
  And neither bark nor bite.

Upon his back he lets you ride,
  And drive about the yard,
And now, while sitting by your side,
To have a bit of bread deny'd
  Is really very hard.

And all your little tricks he'll bear,
  And never seem to mind,
And yet you say you cannot spare,
One bit of breakfast for his share,
  Altho' he is so kind !

BREAKFAST AND PUSS.

Here's my baby's bread and milk,
For her lip, as soft as silk;
Here's the bason, clean and neat;
Here's the spoon of silver sweet;
Here's the stool, and here's the chair,
For my little lady fair.

No, you must not spill it out,
And drop the bread and milk about;
But let it stand before you flat,
And pray, remember pussy cat:
Poor old pussy cat, that purrs
All so patiently for hers.

True, she runs about the house,
Catching, now and then, a mouse,
But, though she thinks it very nice,
That only makes a *tiny* slice;
So don't forget, that you should stop,
And leave poor puss a little drop.

19

THE FLOWER AND THE LADY, ABOUT GETTING UP.

PRETTY flower, tell me why
  All your leaves do open wide,
Every morning, when on high
  The noble sun begins to ride.

This is why, my lady fair,
  If you would the reason know,
For betimes, the pleasant air
  Very cheerfully doth blow.

And the birds on ev'ry tree
  Sing a merry, merry tune;
And the busy honey bee,
  Comes to suck my sugar soon.

This is all the reason why
  I my little leaves undo;
Lady, lady, wake and try,
  If I have not told you true.

FOR A LITTLE GIRL THAT DID NOT LIKE TO BE WASHED.

WHAT! cry to be wash'd, and not love to be clean!
There, go and be dirty, not fit to be seen,
And till you leave off, and I see you have smil'd,
I won't take the trouble to wash such a child.
Suppose I should leave you now, just as you are,
Do you think you'd deserve a sweet kiss from
    papa;
Or to sit on his knee, and learn pretty great A,
With fingers that have not been wash'd all the
    day!

Ah! look at your fingers, you see it is so,
Did you ever behold such a little black row?
And for *once*, you may look at yourself in the
    glass:
There's a face, to belong to a good little lass!
Come, come, then, I see you're beginning to clear,
You won't be so foolish again, will you, dear?

THE FIELD DAISY.

I'M a pretty little thing,
Always coming with the spring,
In the meadows green I'm found,
Peeping just above the ground,
And my stalk is cover'd flat,
With a white and yellow hat.

Little lady, when you pass
Lightly o'er the tender grass,
Skip about, but do not tread
On my meek and healthy head;
For I always seem to say,
" Surly winter's gone away."

PLAYING WITH FIRE.

I've seen a little girl, mamma,
That had got such a dreadful scar,
All down her arms, and neck, and face,
I could not bear to see the place.

Poor little girl! and don't you know
The shocking trick that made her so?
'Twas all because she went and did
A thing her mother had forbid.

For, once, when nobody was by her,
This silly child would play with fire;
And long before her mother came,
Her pin-a-fore was all in flame!

In vain she try'd to put it out,
Till all her clothes were burnt about,
And then she suffer'd ten times more,
All over with the dreadful sore.

For many months, before 'twas cur'd,
Most shocking torments she endur'd;
And even now, in passing by her,
You see what 'tis to play with fire!

THE LITTLE COWARD.

Why, here's a foolish little man!
Laugh at him, Donkey, if you can!
And cat, and dog, and cow, and calf,
Come, ev'ry one of you, and laugh:

For, only think, he runs away,
If honest Donkey does but bray;
And when the bull begins to bellow,
He's like a crazy little fellow!

Poor Brindle cow can hardly pass
Along the hedge, to nip the grass,
Or wag her tail to lash the flies,
But off the little Booby hies!

And when old Tray comes running too,
With bow, wow, wow, for how d'ye do?
And means it all for civil play,
'Tis sure to make him run away!

But all the while you're thinking, may be,
"Ah! well, but this must be a baby."
Oh! cat, and dog, and cow, and calf,
I'm not surpris'd to see you laugh,
He's five years old, and almost half.

A PRETTY THING.

Who am I that shine so bright,
With my pretty yellow light;
Peeping through your curtains grey?
Tell me, little girl, I pray.

When the sun is gone, I rise
In the very silent skies;
And a cloud or two doth skim,
Round about my silver rim.

All the little stars do seem,
Hidden by my brighter beam;
And among them I do ride,
Like a queen in all her pride.

Then the reaper goes along,
Singing forth a merry song;
While I light the shaking leaves,
And the yellow harvest sheaves.

Little girl, consider well,
Who this simple tale doth tell;
And I think you'll guess it soon,
For I only am the moon.

SLEEPY HARRY.

I do not like to go to bed,
Sleepy little Harry said;
So, naughty Betty, go away,
I will not come at all, I say.

O what a silly little fellow!
I should be quite asham'd to tell her;
Then, Betty, you must come and carry,
This very foolish little Harry.

The little birds are better taught.
They go to roosting when they ought;
And all the ducks and fowls, you know,
They went to bed an hour ago.

The little beggar in the street,
Who wanders with his naked feet,
And has not where to lay his head,
O, he'd be *glad* to go to bed.

And now that I am old and grey,
I wander on my lonely way,
And beg my bread from day to day.

But oft I shake my hoary head,
And many a bitter tear I shed,
To think the useless life I've led!

THE LITTLE FISH THAT WOULD NOT DO AS IT WAS BID.

Dear mother, said a little fish,
    Pray, is not that a fly?
I'm very hungry, and I wish
    You'd let me go and try.

Sweet innocent, the mother cry'd,
    And started from her nook,
That horrid fly is put to hide
    The sharpness of the hook!

Now, as I've heard, this little trout
    Was young and foolish too,
And so he thought he'd venture out,
    To see if it were true.

And round about the hook he play'd,
    With many a longing look,
And " Dear me," to himself he said,
    " I'm sure, that's not a *hook*."

" I can but give one little pluck;
    Let's see; and so I will."
So on he went, and lo! it stuck,
    Quite thro' his little gill!

And as he faint and fainter grew,
    With hollow voice he cry'd,
" Dear mother, if I'd minded you,
    I need not now have dy'd! "

THE OLD BEGGAR MAN.

I see an old man sitting there;
His wither'd limbs are almost bare,
And very hoary is his hair.

Old man! why are you sitting so!
For very cold the wind doth blow,
Why don't you to your cottage go?

Ah, master! in the world so wide,
I've no home wherein to hide,
No comfortable fire side!

When I, like you, was young and gay,
I'll tell you what I us'd to say,
" That I would nothing do but play."

And so, instead of being taught
Some useful bus'ness, as I ought,
To play about was all I sought.

22

THE SELFISH SNAILS.

It happen'd that a little snail,
Came crawling with his slimy tail,
   Upon a cabbage stalk;
But two more little snails were there,
Both feasting on this dainty fare,
   Engag'd in friendly talk.

" No, no, you shall not dine with us,
How dare you interrupt us thus ! "
   The greedy snails declare;
So their poor brother they discard,
Who really thinks it very hard,
   He may not have his share.

But selfish folks are sure to know,
They get no good by being so,
   In earnest or in play;
Which these two snails confess'd, no doubt,
When soon the gardener spy'd them out,
   And threw them both away.

SULKING.

Why is Mary standing there !
Leaning down upon a chair,
With pouting lip, and frowning brow :
I wonder what's the matter now !

Come here, my dear, and tell me true,
Is it because I scolded you ?
For doing work so bad and slow,
That you are standing sulking so ?

Why then, indeed, I'm griev'd to see,
That you can so ill-temper'd be;
You make your fault a great deal worse,
By being angry and perverse.

O, how much better it appears,
To see you melting into tears,
And then to hear you humbly say,
" I'll not do so another day."

But when you stand and sulk about,
And look so cross, and cry, and pout,
Why that, my little girl, you know,
Is *worse* than working bad and slow.

THE LITTLE BEGGAR GIRL.

There's a poor beggar going by,
   I see her looking in;
She's just about as big as I,
   Only so very thin.

She has no shoes upon her feet,
   She is so very poor;
And hardly any thing to eat:
   I pity her, I'm sure !

But I have got nice clothes, you know,
   And meat, and bread, and fire;
And you, mamma, that love me so,
   And all that I desire.

If I were forc'd to stroll so far,
   O dear, what should I do !

I wish she had a dear mamma,
  Just such a one as you.

Here, little girl, come back again,
  And hold your ragged hat,
For I shall put a penny in;
  So buy some bread with that.

THE DUNCE OF A KITTEN.

Come, pussy, will you learn to read,
  I've got a pretty book:
Nay, turn this way, you must indeed.—
  Fie, there's a sulky look.

Here is a pretty picture, see,
  An apple and great A:
How stupid you will ever be,
  If you do nought but play.

Come, A, B, C, an easy task,
  What any fool can do:
I will do any thing you ask,
  For dearly I love you.

Now, how I'm vex'd, you are so dull,
  You have not learnt it half:
You will grow up a downright fool,
  And make all people laugh.

Mamma told me so, I declare,
  And made me quite asham'd;
So I resolv'd no pains to spare,
  Nor like a dunce be blam'd.

Well, get along, you naughty Kit,
  And after mice go look;
I'm glad that I have got more wit,
  I love my pretty book.

ONE LITTLE BOY.

I'm a little gentleman,
Play, and ride, and dance I can,
Very handsome clothes I wear,
And I live on dainty fare;
And whenever out I ride,
I've a servant by my side.

And I never, all the day,
Need do any thing but play;
Nor even soil my little hand,
Because I am so very grand;
O! I'm very glad, I'm sure,
I need not labour, like the poor.

For I think I could not bear,
Such old shabby clothes to wear;
To lie upon so hard a bed,
And only live on barley bread;
And what is worse, too, ev'ry day
To have to work as hard as they.

ANOTHER LITTLE BOY.

I'm a little husbandman,
Work and labour hard I can;
I'm as happy all the day
At my work as if 'twere play;
Though I've nothing fine to wear,
Yet for that I do not care.

When to work I go along,
Singing loud my morning song,
With my wallet at my back,
Or my waggon whip to smack;
O, I am as happy then,
As the idle gentlemen.

I've a hearty appetite,
And I soundly sleep at night,
Down I lie content, and say,
" I've been useful all the day.
I'd rather be a plough boy, than
A useless little gentleman."

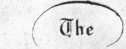

The

COURTSHIP and MARRIAGE

of

JERRY & KITTY;

Illustrated

—— *with* ——

Elegant Engravings.

LONDON:

Published Nov. 20. 1814, by
J. Harris corner of St. Pauls.

1

There was a lad liv'd on a hill
Jerry alone Jerry alone
There was a Lad liv'd on a hill
Jerry alone liv'd he,
There was a Lad liv'd on a hill
And a Lady down by the Mill,
Kitty Mc Carey she was his deary
Kitty Mc Carey was she.

2

When he saw her first she was curling her Wig
Jerry alone Jerry alone
When he saw her first she was curling her Wig
Peeping Jerry was he.
When he saw her first she was curling her Wig
And it pleas'd her so that she danc'd a Jig.
Kitty Mc Carey, vain little Carey
Proud of her Wig was she.

3

This Lad he went to his Mother and cry'd
Jerry alone Jerry alone
This Lad he went to his Mother and cry'd
Blubbering Jerry was he.
Pray let me try to make her my Bride
In my foraging Cap and my Sword by my side
I'll say Kitty Carey you are my deary
Can you object to me?

4

His Mother was mov'd by his pitiful face
   Jerry go down Jerry go down
His Mother was mov'd by his pitiful face
   And Jerry go down said she.
So away he went to the door of the Hall
And there he did both knock and call,
Kitty Mc Carey yon are my deary
   Prithee come down to me.

5

Miss Kitty his dear walk'd stately down
   Jerry alone Jerry alone
Miss Kitty his dear walk'd stately down
   Jerry alone saw she.
Miss Kitty his dear walk'd stately down
In a sarsenet cloak and a calico Gown,
Kitty Mc Carey his pretty deary
   Alamode Kitty was she,

6

I am come Miss for to see
   Jerry was bold Jerry was bold
I am come Miss for to see
   Jerry spoke bold to she.
I am come Miss for to see
If that you can fancy me
You are my fancy
Parlez-vous François?
   Allez-vous-en said she.

7

For I can give yon no answer to that
   Jerry go home Jerry go home
I can give yon no answer to that
   So Jerry go home said she
But I'll take off my Cloak and my Hat
And then I'll ask my Uncle Matt.
Kitty Mc Carey my little deary
   I will not go home said he.

8

If you wont go home come in and dine
    Jerry alone Jerry alone,
If you won't go home come in and dine
    Jerry come dine with me;
And you shall have a Turkey and chine
A Bowl of Punch and a bottle of Wine.
Oh! rare Miss Carey — Jolly Miss Carey
Jovial Miss Kitty was she.

9

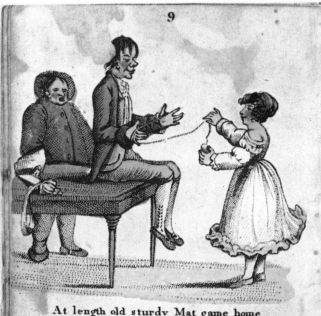

At length old sturdy Mat came home
    Jerry employ'd Jerry employ'd
At length old sturdy Mat came home
    Busy Jerry was he.
At length old sturdy Mat came home
Saying who's been here since Ive been gone?
Kitty Mc Carey my little deary
Kitty my Loye tell me.

10

No one but this fine Gentleman
    Jerry ashamd Jerry ashamd
No one but this fine Gentleman
    Jerry alone you see.
No one but this fine Gentleman
May I have him if I can?
Uncle my deary your Kitty Carey
Has a great mind to he.

11

Old Uncle Mat gave his consent
    Jerry was glad Jerry was glad
Old Uncle Mat gave his consent
    That they should married be.
Old Uncle Mat gave his consent
And so away to Church they went
Kitty Mc Carey — Jerry O' Leary
What a sweet pair are we!!

And when Mrs Leary was brought to bed
   Jerry Papa, Jerry Papa,
And when Mrs Leary was brought to bed,
   Jerry went up to see
His fine little boy with two eyes in his head,
One was green, the other was red,
   Oh Kitty my deary — Master O'Leary
   What a sweet babe was he !!

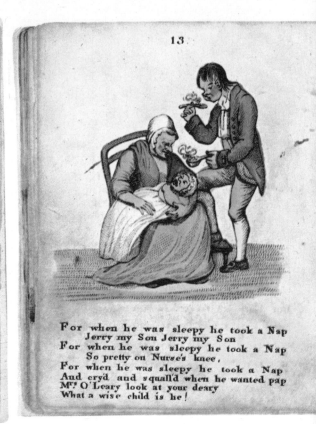

For when he was sleepy he took a Nap
   Jerry my Son Jerry my Son
For when he was sleepy he took a Nap
   So pretty on Nurse's knee,
For when he was sleepy he took a Nap
And cry'd and squall'd when he wanted pap
   Mrs O'Leary look at your deary
   What a wise child is he !

But Kitty and Jerry grew tir'd of home
   Kitty of he, Jerry of she
They search'd all the Maps for a place where tor
   For they wish'd on a ramble to be
Old Ireland both had a mind to see
And thought they'd pop over to Donaghadee
   Mrs O'Leary she was quite weary
   Sick of the Sea was she.

And Jerry was sick of his sweet little Wife
   Jerry alone Jerry alone
Jerry was sick of his dear little Wife
   And wish'd he alone could be;
So he told her the Sea was not very deep
And popp'd her in when she went up to peep.
   Oh! Fye Mr Leary, where is your deary?
   —— Just gone a bathing said he.

A new Book for the Improvement of Young Gentlemen and Ladies.

FILIAL DUTY,

RECOMMENDED and ENFORC'D,

By a VARIETY of INSTRUCTIVE and ENTERTAINING STORIES,

O F

CHILDREN who have been remarkable for AFFECTION to their PARENTS;

A L S O

An ACCOUNT of some striking INSTANCES of CHILDREN, who have behaved in an UNDUTIFUL, and UNNATURAL Manner to their PARENTS.

The whole founded on HISTORICAL FACTS.

L O N D O N:

Printed for F. NEWBERY, the CORNER of St. PAUL'S CHURCH YARD.

A CHILD eight years of age, gave a striking proof of filial tenderness. His parents were so poor, that they were even destitute of a coverlid to defend them in the summer from the flies: this infant stript himself naked to the waist, and stood by the side of the bed, exposing his delicate skin to the flies, without driving them away: *when they are filled with my blood, said he, they will let my parents be at rest.*

MINSUN lost his mother when he was very young, his father took another wife, by whom he had two children; Minsun was very severely treated by this step-mother, but never complained. He one day fell in a swoon at his father's feet, who then knew the cause of it, and was going to dismiss the unnatural step-mother, but Minsun hindered him. My father, said he, there are three children of us, I am the only one who suffers, but if you send your wife away, we must all suffer. The father was touched with these words, and the step-mother being informed of them, became an affectionate parent to Minsun.

A WOMAN of family was condemned to be strangled; she was sent to prison, in order to suffer the sentence passed upon her; the gaoler, commiserating her unhappy case, could not put her to death, he determined to let her die of hunger, he permitted her daughter to visit her, first strictly searching her, to see that she brought no provisions; this continuing some time, he could not conceive by what means his prisoner subsisted so long without nourishment. His suspicions fell upon the daughter, and secreting himself where she could not see him, determined the next time she came to condole with her unhappy parent, if possible to find out the manner by which she prolonged her existence. This amiable young woman, next morning gave him the desired opportunity, when, to his unspeakable surprise, he discovered this Phœnix of filial affection, recruiting the feeble dugs of remaining life in her aged parent, with the milk from her own breasts. Astonished at such an instance of piety, and ingenuity, he told the circumstance to the chief magistrate, who related it to the assembly of the people; in consequence of which, the mother was pardoned, and a decree passed, that she and her virtuous daughter, should be maintained, during the rest of their lives, at the public charge, and a temple dedicated to piety, should be erected on the spot, to perpetuate this event to future ages.

ANN ROSE was a good girl; she did not cry when she was dressed and washed; she used to like to play in the field, and run and pick up flowers, and put them in her frock, to smell how sweet they were; and she went with the maid to see her milk the cow, and feed the ducks. And in the field there were two sheep, and four small lambs. The sheep were quite tame, and so were the lambs; they all ran to ANN as soon as they saw her in the field; for she used to give them

some leaves to eat; and they would eat out of her hand; but they did not bite her, for they did not want to hurt her; but they loved her for being so kind as to feed them.

A BOY fell in a pond. He had not sunk quite out of sight, before a man who was near the pond saw him, and ran to help him, and with a great deal of pains at last got him out, and laid him down upon the ground. He did not lie there long, for he soon got well enough to walk home. When his Papa and Mamma saw him so wet, they were both angry with him, and chid

him a great deal; for they had told him not to go near the water, or ice, for fear he should fall in. And as they had told him so before, he ought not, you know, to have gone. So his Papa said, if he would not be good, and mind what was said to him, and do as he was bid, he should not go out at all. He then tied his legs and arms with a piece of string, and made him sit still all the rest of the day, till it was time to go to-bed. The next morning, when he got up, he told his

Papa and Mamma, that he would be good, and mind what they said to him; and he asked them to be so kind as to kiss him, and he would not be naughty any more: so they both did kiss him, which made him very happy.

AS a little girl was walking in the road, she found a box. O! said she, what a nice box I have found? So she picked it up, and took off the lid, and saw in it a nice doll, and a ball, and a bird: not a live bird, but a play-thing, one made of

wood; and the name of it was a Lark. It could not sing, because it was not alive; but live Larks sing very well, and so do Black Birds, but Crows do not sing, they only saw caw, caw, caw. The little girl went home with the box in her hand, and showed it to her Mamma. Look here! said she, see what fine things I have found! a doll! and a ball! and a wooden bird called a Lark! They are very nice, said her Mamma, take care

you do not spoil, break, or dirt them, for if you do, they will not look so well as they do now.

A Wasp one day flew upon a boy, and did not intend to hurt him; but the silly child cried and screamed as loud as he could squall, and would not wait till the wasp would fly off; but beat it with his hand, which made it very angry, and it thought the boy was going to kill it; so then it stung him, and made his hand sore; but it would not have stung the boy, if he had not first hurt it;

for wasps do not sting if they are not hurt. The boy's hand was in great pain, and he did not know what to do with it, or how to cure it. But a kind man saw him, and said, Do not cry, little boy, I will rub it with some oil, and that will do it good. Thank you, Sir, said the boy, you are very kind to rub my hand, and to try to make it well. I shall be glad, said the man, to cure it for you this time; but I beg you will not cry if a wasp should come upon you any more, for it will not sting you, if you let it quite alone, and do not touch it; but will soon fly from you, and not hurt you at all.

AFTER James Green had read his book, he had two plums and a bun given him for being a good boy: but he did not eat them all himself; for he gave half the bun and one of his plums to his dear little sister Jane; and then he had but half a bun and one plum left for himself; but he was so kind, that he gave some of that to his cat and dog; both of which he was very fond of, for they were good-natured, and quite clean, and used to

walk after him wherever he went. When he played in the garden, they run with him; and if he stood still, they stopped close to him; and when he moved, they went with him. The little cat's name was Snip, and the dog he called Snap. To be sure, they were odd names, but he chose to call them so; and he used to say, if he had any more dogs, he would call them by some other strange names, though he could not tell what they should be. But his Papa and Mamma did not choose he should have more than one cat and one dog at a time.

31

AS a bird one day was flying to look for some food for its young ones to eat, a boy, who had a gun in his hand, saw it, and shot the poor thing through its head, and down it fell to the ground. The boy then ran to it, and picked it up; and when he saw that it was dead, he gave it to his dog to eat. How naughty it was to kill the poor thing, which never did any harm in all its life; and to take it from all its young ones, which were in the nest wanting it to come back and feed them. They could not think why it stayed so long from them, and kept chirp, chirping till they were quite tired. And at night they grew so cold for want of their mother to cover them, that they did not know what to do. There were five in the nest, and two of them were starved to death with cold and hunger in the night; the other three lived till the next morning, when getting to the edge of the nest, to look if they could see their mother, two of them fell out and broke their little bones. They lay in great pain for some time upon the ground, but could not move; for they were too young to hop or fly. At last a hog that was going that way, and passed by the tree from which they had fallen, saw them on the ground, and eat them up, and so put them out of their pain; or else how long they would have laid in that sad way, I cannot tell. But the other poor thing that was left in the nest, did not so soon die, for it lived all day long, very cold, and in much pain for want of something to eat: it kept chirping as long as it could, in hopes its mother would hear it; at last when it was quite tired, it lay still at the bottom of the nest: and in the night it rained fast, and the wind blew, so it died with cold, just as it began to grow day-light again. So there was an

end of five nice young birds, which all died in such a painful way, because a cross boy shot their poor mother.

A LITTLE boy once climbed up a tree to get a bough; and just as he had cut it off, his foot slipped, and down he fell with it in his hand. He lay for some time still, so much frightened, that he scarcely knew if he was hurt or not. At last he saw his Papa ride by on horse-back, so up he jumped, ran to him, and called out, Pray, Sir, take me up! Pray, Sir, let me ride! His Papa was very good and kind, so he stooped down and took him up, and let him have a nice long ride. As they went along, they met an old man, who was very poor, and asked them to give him some bread. The little boy told him he had no bread, but he had a farthing, and if he pleased he would give him that. So the old man thanked him, and said he should be glad of it, as it would buy him a small piece of bread, and a little bit was better than none. The child then gave him the farthing: the old man thanked him, pulled off his hat, made him a bow, and walked on. His father then told him, that he was much pleased to see him so kind as to give his farthing to help the poor man. I held my tongue, said he, and did not speak for the sake of hearing what you had to say: and I was glad to find you spoke so good-natured. But as a farthing will buy but a very small bit of bread, I will turn back and ride after him, and give him twopence, which is as much as eight farthings. Pray, Sir, make haste and go after him, said the boy, for fear he should be gone. So they turned about, and gave him the two-pence. The poor man was much rejoiced to have it, and thanked them a great many times. And after that they rode home again.

A MAN going along with a basket upon his head full of tarts and buns dropped some of them out; and a boy who was near him, and saw them fall, picked them up, and ran to him, and gave them all to him again. Thank you, my dear, said the man, why did you not eat them yourself? Because that would not have been right, said the boy, for they are not mine, and I must not take what is not my own. That is true, said the man, and you did quite right to bring them to me; but as you have been so good, I will give you two tarts and a bun for yourself. The man then gave the boy two tarts and a bun; for which he thanked him, and took them home, and gave

one tart and half his bun to his brother, as every child who is good and likes to be loved will do: for brothers and sisters should always give some of their things to each other, and try to please one another. After this good little boy was gone, the man with the tarts dropped some more and another boy saw them fall, and ran to pick them up; but he did not do like the other good boy; for instead of giving them to the man, he began to eat them. As he was biting them, the man turned round and saw him. Pray, where did you get those tarts? said he. I picked them up, answered the boy, and I ate them because I liked them. But they are mine, said the man; you saw me drop them, and you should have brought them to me; but since you behave so like a thief, and eat what you know is not your own, I shall take them away, and thrash you, that you may

learn not to do so again. The man then took his basket from off his head, went to the boy, took from him the tarts, and beat him with a stick he had in his hand. The boy cried sadly, and wished he had been good; for it is much better to be good than naughty; and so all children will find.

A MAN who had two sons, took them one day into a field; and holding a cake in his hand, told them, he would give it to him who would first get to the hedge, which was on the other side of the field. So they both set off to run as fast as they could; and both would have reached the hedge at the same time, if TOM's foot had not slipped, which made him fall down, and by that means JOHN got there first. His father gave him the cake, as he had said he would. JOHN thanked him, and took it; but he gave his brother half of it; for he said, that if his own foot had slipped and thrown him down, he should have liked TOM

to have given him some, and so he thought Tom would like some of his. And all good children should behave the same, and at all times do to each other what they would like to be done to themselves; for that is the way to make people love them.

A MAN once kept a monkey, which he was very fond of; but it did so much mischief that at last he was quite tired of it, and gave it away. It was not tied up, but used to run about where it pleased. Sometimes it would watch the cook when she was getting dinner, sometimes the footman whilst he was combing his master's wigs, and sometimes it sat by the maids whilst they were at work. One day when it had been in the kitchen, and seen the cook put a pudding into the pot to boil, it watched her till she stepped into the yard to get something she wanted, and before she came back, it ran up stairs and fetched down one of its master's wigs, which he popped into the same pot where the pudding was, before the cook came back. After Pug had done this trick, he walked up stairs again, and found one of the maids cleaning the stove with brick-dust. She did not think about the monkey, and soon went out of the room; and the moment she was gone, Pug took the brick-dust and rubbed all the nice clean tables and chairs with it, till it quite spoiled them. When the maid came back, she beat poor Pug for making so much dirt, and doing such mischief, and sent him down stairs. Then he ran into the chicken-yard, and caught two or three of the fowls, and pulled all their feathers off. After that, he went into the coal-hole and filled both his hands and mouth with coals, and

then ran and put them into the flour-tub; and such kind of tricks he used to play all day long. But had you seen the cook when she went to take up the pudding, I am sure you would have laughed; for instead of taking up a pudding, out came an old boiled wig. Heigh-day! said she, what have I got here? I am sure I put a very nice pudding into the pot, but I cannot say this looks nice; I will go show it to my master. She then took it at the end of a fork to her master. Look here, Sir! said she, is not this one of your wigs? I am sure I put a nice pudding into the pot, but it is changed into a wig. No, said her master, the pudding is not changed, but my poor wig is sadly changed into a sop, and is quite spoiled. The monkey has done it; and he does so many tricks, that I will keep him no longer, but give him away to-day. So, after dinner, he took it to a lady who liked monkeys; but she tied it up, and would not let it run about any more.

THERE was once a little boy whose name was Peter, and he had a little brother, named Charles. They were both so good, that they were loved by all persons who knew them; and as they always did what they were told to do, their friends used to call them by the name of the two little Do-wells. One day as they were walking in the fields with their Mamma and sister Mary, they saw a party of school boys playing at trap-ball; and as one of them, whose name was Tom Stout, was going to strike the ball, he hit poor little Peter on the face with the bat he had in his hand, and it made his nose bleed

sadly. His brother and sister were both much frightened; but when his Mamma found that it would soon be well again, they dried their tears, and tried to comfort poor PETER, for they loved him very much, and were very sorry that he had been hurt. After he had sat in his Mamma's lap a little while, and the blood was stopped, he went to play again, but took care for the future not to stand too near to great boys when they were playing with any thing in their hands which might hurt him.

Things
by Their Right Names

Charles. PAPA, you grow very lazy. Last winter you used to tell us stories, and now you never tell us any; and we are all got round the fire quite ready to hear you. Pray, dear papa, let us have a very pretty one?

Father. With all my heart—What shall it be?

C. A bloody murder, papa!

F. A bloody murder! Well then—Once upon a time, some men, dressed all alike . . . .

C. With black crapes over their faces.

F. No; they had steel caps on:—having crossed a dark heath, wound cautiously along the skirts of a deep forest . . .

C. They were ill-looking fellows, I dare say.

F. I cannot say so; on the contrary, they were tall personable men as most one shall see:—leaving on their right hand an old ruined tower on the hill . . .

C. At midnight, just as the clock struck twelve; was it not, papa?

F. No, really; it was on a fine balmy summer's morning:—and moved forwards, one behind another . . .

C. As still as death, creeping along under the hedges.

F. On the contrary—they walked remarkably upright; and so far from endeavouring to be hushed and still, they made a loud noise as they came along, with several sorts of instruments.

C. But, papa, they would be found out immediately.

F. They did not seem to wish to conceal themselves: on the contrary, they gloried in what they were about.—They moved forwards, I say, to a large plain, where stood a neat pretty village, which they set on fire . . .

C. Set a village on fire? wicked wretches!

F. And while it was burning, they murdered—twenty thousand men.

C. O fie! papa! You do not intend I should believe this! I thought all along you were making up a tale, as you often do; but you shall not catch me this time. What! they lay still, I suppose, and let these fellows cut their throats!

F. No, truly—they resisted as long as they could.

C. How should these men kill twenty thousand people, pray?

F. Why not? the *murderers* were thirty thousand.

C. O, now I have found you out. You mean a BATTLE.

F. Indeed I do. I do not know of any *murders* half so bloody.

Little Rhymes for Little Folks

THE DOG TRIM

There was once a nice little dog, Trim,
  Who ne'er had ill temper or whim ;
He could sit up and dance,
  Could run, skip, and prance—
Who would not like little dog Trim ?

THE LITTLE LAMBS

Those dear little lambs, how pretty they look,
  All drinking the water down at the brook ;
Good bye, pretty lambs ! there, now go to play,
  We'll see you again on some other day.

LITTLE FANNY

So, Fanny, my love
  You've a pretty new frock,
I wish you your health, dear, to wear it ;
  'Tis so very neat,
  And it fits you so well,
You'll be careful, I hope, not to tear it.

THE WINDMILL

Blow, wind, blow ; and go, mill, go,
That the miller may grind his corn ;
  That the baker may take it
  And into rolls make it,
And send us some hot in the morn.

THE LITTLE DONKEY

I'm a poor little Donkey,
  And work very hard,
To my sighs and fatigues
  Master pays no regard ;
Yet for him would I toil,
  And do always my best,
Would he speak to me kindly,
  And give me some rest.

FANNY AND HER CAT

Come here, little Puss,
  And I'll make you quite smart,
You shall wear this gold chain,
  And I'll wear this fine heart ;
And when we are drest,
  My dear Aunty shall see
Who then will look best,
  Little Pussy or me !

LITTLE PUSS

As Pussy sat upon the step,
  Taking the nice fresh air,
A neighbour's little dog came by,
  Ah, Pussy, are you there ?
Good morning, Mistress Pussy Cat,
  Come, tell me how you do ?
Quite well, I thank you, Puss replied ;
  Now tell me how are you ?

THE COCK

The Cock crows in the morn
  To tell us to rise,
And that he who lies late
  Will never be wise :
For heavy and stupid,
  He can't learn his book,
So long as he lives
  Like a Dunce he must look.

LITTLE FREDDY

Here comes little Fred,
  In his pretty new clothes,
Little trowsers and boots,
  And nice little white hose ;
His frock's thrown aside,
  Now he'll do all he can
To be good and be clever,
  And grow up a man.

THE ROCKING HORSE

When Charles has done reading
  His book every day,
He goes out with his hoop
  In the garden to play ;
Or, his whip in his hand,
  Quickly mounts up across,
And then gallops away
  On his fine Rocking horse.

A PLEASANT RIDE

As the weather is fine,
  I will take a nice ride,
And Martha and Fanny
  Shall sit by my side :
We'll drive by the sea,
  And enjoy the fresh air,
Then walk to the pier,
  And see who is there.

A PLEASANT WALK

In the sweet month of May,
  When the fields look so green,
Little lambs skip and play,
  And nice flowers can be seen ;
Then the sun shines so bright,
  And the days are so long,
And the dear little birds
  Charm the groves with their song.

Early Seeds to Produce Spring Flowers

Gathering Apples.

WHAT a noble tree, and what an abundance of fruit! The gatherers will not labour in vain. I say labour, for it is not their object to gather a few, just to indulge their own appetites. No! the produce of this tree is a little fortune to its owner. By the sale of those apples, he will pay the rent of his neat, though homely cottage; and, to his honest mind, this will be the sweetest in its flavor.

Making Wine.

LOOK in the background of this picture; is it a regiment we see, all marshalled in a row? No, the array is of a far more innocent nature. The scene is that of a vintage, or the process of gathering grapes; and what at first sight looked like bayonets, is a row of vines, from which the vintagers are stripping the fruit. The pretty maid in the straw hat is emptying her basket

into that large tub, and the man, as you may observe, presses the grapes with his feet; but there is much more to be done before we can get this same wine into our cellar.

Greediness defeated.

THIS is a speaking picture, and tells its own story. Here is a silly child, whose greediness is so great, that she has not patience to await the cooling of her bread and milk; and the consequence is, that she has burned her mouth severely. Her papa seems to be chiding her, and no wonder, for she looks much too old to be guilty of so disgusting a habit. Why should we laugh at pigs and ducks for their greediness, when children, who can both speak and think, act in the same manner as those animals?

Catching Fish.

HERE are flat fish and haddock just out of the water. These poor men have toiled hard for them, and I hope will carry them to a good market. The life of fishermen is exposed to many toils and dangers; out in all weathers, they often brave the storm when the sea runs mountains high, and, alas! are sometimes overwhelmed by the foaming waves, and sink to rise no more! Think, then, how anxious their poor families must feel, while they are fishing, to maintain them! I am glad to see these good men safe on the beach, and I hope those in the distance, who have not yet drawn their nets, may be as fortunate.

The Pony and his Rider.

Who could desire to mount a prettier animal than the one represented in the picture? How handsomely he is spotted, and what a long and flowing tail he has! His pace, too, is quite graceful; and really the young rider seems to manage him with much ability. Observe how gently he uses the whip! He is right; kind usage will do more than angry words and blows.

A Boys' School.

What is so delightful as knowledge? Solomon, who was the wisest of mankind, reckoned wisdom above all wordly riches, for it is lasting wealth.

Did you ever see a clever and studious child unhappy? Certainly not; it is only the idle and wilfully ignorant who are wretched. In the group before us, all are engaged; even that little fellow on the ground, who, on a first view, may appear idle, will not shrink from our observation. Look well into his countenance, and you will perceive that he is learning his lesson by heart, and his keen eye does not bespeak a want of memory. The boy to whom the schoolmaster is talking has not, I fear, learned his lesson quite correctly; for his master seems to be admonishing him to greater diligence, and the young student will, no doubt, be more careful another time.

It is really great kindness in a man of sense and learning to give up his time, and to devote his talents to the purpose of teaching children to be wise and good; and it is surely very ungrateful not to repay such care by a strict attention to all he says; for how could the young ever gain knowledge, if they were not taught by their elders?

A Newfoundland Dog preserving a Child from a watery Grave.

This is a sad, yet pleasing scene; an innocent babe saved, from drowning, by that noble and sensible animal, a dog.

This kind creature is of the Newfoundland breed; very large and strong. His black and white shaggy coat, and handsome full tail, look very grand. He is of a valuable species, whose attachment to mankind will lead them into the greatest perils; and they will buffet with the waves a long time before they will let their burden drop.

In the picture he seems to be in fresh water, and carries his charge with ease.

Ah! foolish child, I fear you were playing on the margin of the stream, and, venturing too near, slipped into the smooth water, that seemed to you like a looking-glass; but, thanks to honest Cato, you are now safe, and will soon be as lively as ever. Yet, young as you appear, I hope this narrow escape may dwell in your memory, and that, while you thank Providence for its divine protection, you will not forget your obligation to the generous dumb animal which has thus restored you to your sorrowing friends.

A Fire-Escape Ladder.

ARE you not glad to see this poor man and his child so far on the road to safety? There is another person just behind him, who will, no doubt, escape too; thanks to the humane inventor of the ladder you see here! The flames would not have allowed another minute's stay in the chamber they have left; and how could they have reached the ground but by throwing themselves from the windows? Had they done so, they might have been killed on the spot, or at least have broken their limbs, and, perhaps, have been cripples all the rest of their lives.

Effects of Climbing.

HERE is an instructive result of a silly habit.

We certainly do not envy the young gentleman his present situation. He does not look very comfortable; but, as it was his own seeking, he has no right to complain. By the time he is quite on the ground, and the chair upon him, he will have pain enough to make him remember the folly of his conduct. If children had no better way of employing time than this, it would be well if they slept all their lives; but we know they have plenty of books to improve their minds, and others that will amuse their fancies. They can also walk in the fields, work in their gardens, or listen to the conversation of their friends; in short, do any thing rather than mischief. We may be merry, and enjoy many innocent and diverting sports, without running into danger. A sensible boy can never be at a loss for a pleasant pursuit. The idle may prefer tricks of this kind, because they do not trouble the mind; but if they will just look at the picture before them, they will find that climbing has more danger than study, and that a lively story-book possesses more entertainment, than can be found in a broken head or a cut nose.

Innocent Sports.

LOOK at this smart little fellow; how neatly he skips! He must have practised much, or he could not manage the rope so gracefully. Skipping is a lively exercise, and very good for the health; so is hoop-trundling. See that boy in the background; he runs with all his might, and still keeps trundling the hoop. You may observe, he holds the stick in his left hand; as much as to say, he is so expert, that he can use it as well with one hand as the other. To the left, we may perceive three more little fellows playing at top-spinning, and at marbles. Boys can never be dull, when they have such various methods of engaging their leisure hours.

Falsehood Punished.

Did you ever see a countenance so full of terror ? Cowardly boy, you were not afraid to tell a falsehood, but you tremble at the punishment it justly deserves. How angry his papa looks ! He must indeed be sorely vexed by such conduct in his child, who is quite old enough to be sensible of the wickedness of a lie. This vile habit should be checked in time, otherwise it will lead to crimes of the worst kind. We cannot put any trust in the word of a liar; no, we disbelieve and shun him; he is despised by all.

The Heedless Girl.

A sad disaster, indeed ! Here is a pretty frock spoiled, and a new carpet likewise; well may the heedless girl hang her head and shed tears. The attitude of her mamma seems to reprove her for doing what she was forbidden to do; so that she has been disobedient, as well as heedless.

On little Harry's christ'ning day,
Jane, dress'd in all her best array,
Was waiting till the parson came,
To give the pretty babe a name.

Her father's inkstand caught her eye;
Jane dipp'd a pen in ink, to try
If she could write,—though well she knew
Her father's censure would ensue.

But, like some other children, Jane
Thought she would dip it once again;
At length, the inkstand she o'erset,
And her new frock, with ink, was wet.

I need not tell what tears she shed;
How early she was sent to bed,
That Harry's christ'ning day went on,
Enjoy'd by all but Jane alone !

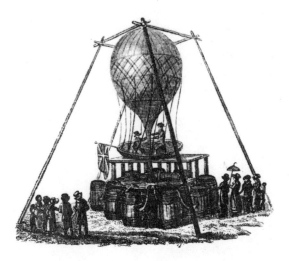

Filling a Balloon.

This is indeed a curious sight, and well worth the walk we have taken to see it. How anxiously the good folks are watching the process of filling ! This balloon is made of oiled silk, and then filled with gas, by means of pipes, as you see in the picture, from the tubs placed around the scaffold. When the balloon is quite full, the cords which fasten it down will be loosened, and then it will ascend gracefully into the air, until we lose sight of it among the clouds. I imagine we should not like to exchange situations with the bold adventurers who mean to journey through the air like birds; for, though we allow they possess courage, and no doubt will see many fine prospects during their excursions, there is always danger in such trials. The balloon may burst, or take fire.

43

Fatal Effects of Fire.

It does indeed fill our hearts with dread, to
behold the devouring elements so near to a
fellow-creature, as these flames appear to be; but
we will hope, that the good woman and her little
boy may escape through that open window from
which a man is lowering a table.

A fire is so terrible an evil, that we cannot
be too careful in avoiding it. We all know its
dreadful powers, yet how often does it happen
from a careless action or a mischievous trick!

Aversion to Physic overcome.

William, when sick and ill,
   Long'd to be free from pain,
Yet would not take one pill
   To make him well again.

But his young brother, John,
   Took what the doctor gave,
And soon his pains were gone,
   While Will was near his grave.

Then eagerly he sought
   What he had spurn'd so long;
By tedious sickness taught
   How far he acted wrong.

Building a House.

How many parts there are in a house, and how
much labour it requires to complete a good one!
First comes the bricklayer, with his mortar and
bricks; then the carpenter, with beams, joists,
and framework; then the glazier, with the windows. All these put together will make building
appear a great undertaking; and, when the house
is finished, our purses, I fear, will be almost
empty.

The tiny Equipage.

Young lady, be not in a hurry; we shall get
out of your way with all speed. I rather think
we are more likely to run over you and your
equipage, than to be run over ourselves; but
this is not said in disrespect, for really we quite
admire your carriage, and the noble animals attached to it. Are you taking an airing, or going
on a tour? If the latter, I beg you will notice all
that is worthy of observation in the course of your
travels, and give us an account of the same, when
you return.

The Daisy

The Giddy Girl.

Miss Helen was always too giddy to heed
  What her mother had told her to shun;
For frequently, over the street in full speed,
  She would cross where the carriages run.

And out she would go to a very deep well,
  To look at the water below;
How naughty! to run to a dangerous well,
  Where her mother forbade her to go!

One morning, intending to take but one peep,
  Her foot slipp'd away from the ground;
Unhappy misfortune! the water was deep,
  And giddy Miss Helen was drown'd.

The Good Scholar.

Joseph West had been told,
That if, when he grew old,
He had not learnt rightly to spell,
Though his writing were good,
'T would not be understood:
And Joe said, " I will learn my task well."

  And he made it a rule
  To be silent at school,

And what do you think came to pass?
  Why, he learnt it so fast,
  That, from being the last,
He soon was the first in the class.

Dressed or Undressed.

When children are naughty, and will not be
    dressed,
  Pray, what do you think is the way?
Why, often I really believe it is best
  To keep them in night-clothes all day!

But then they can have no good breakfast to eat,
  Nor walk with their mother or aunt;
At dinner they 'll have neither pudding nor meat,
  Nor any thing else that they want.

Then who would be naughty, and sit all the day
  In night-clothes unfit to be seen?
And pray, who would lose all their pudding and
    play,
  For not being dressed neat and clean?

Miss Peggy.

As Peggy was crying aloud for a cake,
Which her mother had said she should fetch from
  the wake,

A gentleman knock'd at the door;
He enter'd the parlour and show'd much surprise,
That it really was Peggy who made all the noise,
For he never had heard her before.

Miss Peggy ashamed, and to hide her disgrace,
Took hold of her frock, and quite cover'd her face,
For she knew she was naughty just then;
And, instantly wiping the tears from her eyes,
She promised her mother to make no more noise,
And kiss'd her again and again.

Politeness.

Good little boys should never say,
    "I will," and "Give me these;"
Oh, no! that never is the way,
    But, "Mother, if you please."
And, "If you please," to sister Ann,
    Good boys to say are ready;
And, "Yes, Sir," to a gentleman,
    And, "Yes, Ma'am," to a lady.

Naughty Sam.

Tom and Charles once took a walk,
    To see a pretty lamb;
And, as they went, began to talk
    Of little naughty Sam,

Who beat his younger brother, Bill,
    And threw him in the dirt;
And when his poor Mamma was ill,
    He teased her for a squirt.

"And I," said Tom, "won't play with Sam,
    Although he has a top:"
But here the pretty little lamb
    To talking put a stop.

Charity.

Do you see that old beggar who stands at the
    door?
Do not send him away—we must pity the poor.
Oh! see how he shivers!—he's hungry and cold!
For people can't work when they grow very old.

Go, set near the fire a table and seat,
And Betty shall bring him some bread and some
    meat:
I hope my dear children will always be kind,
Whenever they meet with the aged and blind.

The Dizzy Girl.

As Frances was playing, and turning around,
Her head grew so giddy, she fell to the ground;
    'T was well that she was not much hurt:
But, O what a pity! her frock was so soil'd,

That had you beheld the unfortunate child,
　　You had seen her all cover'd with dirt.

Her mother was sorry, and said, " Do not cry,
And Mary shall wash you, and make you quite
　　　　dry,
　　If you'll promise to turn round no more."
" What, not in the parlour ? " the little girl said:
" No, not in the parlour; for lately I read
　　Of a girl who was hurt with the door.

" She was playing and turning, until her poor
　　head
Fell against the hard door, and it very much bled:
　　And I heard Dr. Camomile tell,
That he put on a plaster, and cover'd it up;
That he gave her some tea, that was bitter to sup,
　　Or perhaps it had never been well."

Frighted by a Cow.

A very young lady,
　　With Susan the maid,
Who carries the baby,
　　Were one day afraid.

They saw a Cow feeding,
　　Quite harmless and still:
Yet scream'd, without heeding
　　The Man at the Mill;

Who, seeing their flutter,
　　Said, " Cows do no harm;
But send you good butter
　　And milk from the farm."

Careless Maria.

Maria was a careless child,
　　And grieved her friends by this:
　　　　Where'er she went,
　　　　Her clothes were rent,
　　Her hat and bonnet spoil'd,
　　A careless little Miss !

Her gloves and mits were often lost,
　　Her tippet sadly soil'd;
　　　　You might have seen,
　　　　Where she had been,
　　For toys all round were toss'd,
　　Oh, what a careless child !

One day her uncle bought a toy,
　　That round and round would twirl
　　　　But when he found
　　　　The litter'd ground,
　　He said, " I don't tee-totums buy
　　For such a careless girl ! "

Miss Sophia.

Miss Sophy, one fine sunny day,
Left her work and ran away;
When soon she reached the garden-gate,
Which finding lock'd, she would not wait,
But tried to climb and scramble o'er
A gate as high as any door.

But little girls should never climb,
And Sophy won't another time;
For when, upon the highest rail,

Her frock was caught upon a nail,
She lost her hold, and, sad to tell,
Was hurt and bruised—for down she fell.

Lucy and Dicky.

Miss Lucy was a charming child,
　She never said, " I won't;"
If little Dick her playthings spoil'd,
　She said, " Pray, Dicky, don't ! "

He took her waxen doll one day,
　And bang'd it round and round;
Then tore its legs and arms away,
　And threw them on the ground.

His good mamma was angry quite,
　And Lucy's tears ran down;
But Dick went supperless that night,
　And since has better grown.

The New Penny.

Miss Ann saw a man,
　Quite poor, at a door,
And Ann had a pretty new Penny;
　Now this the kind Miss
　Threw pat in his hat,
Although she was left without any.

She meant, as she went,
　To stop at a shop,
Where cakes she had seen a great many;
　And buy a fruit-pie,
　Or take home a cake,
By spending her pretty new penny.

But well I can tell,
　When Ann gave the man
Her money, she wish'd not for any;
　He said, " I've no bread,"
　She heard, and preferr'd
To give him her pretty new penny.

The Fan.

Maria's aunt, who lived in town,
　Once wrote a letter to her niece;
And sent, wrapp'd up, a new half-crown,
　Besides a pretty pocket-piece.

Maria jump'd with joy, and ran
　To tell her sister the good news;
She said, " I mean to buy a fan,
　Come, come along with me to choose."

They quickly tied their hats, and talk'd
　Of yellow, lilac, pink, and green;
But far the sisters had not walk'd,
　Before the saddest sight was seen.

Upon the ground a poor lame man,
　Helpless and old, had tumbled down,
She thought no more about the fan,
But gave to him her new half-crown.

Falsehood Corrected.

WHEN Jacky drown'd our poor cat Tib,
He told a very naughty fib,
    And said he had not drown'd her;
But truth is always soon found out—
No one but Jack had been about
    The place where Thomas found her.

And Thomas saw him with the cat,
(Though Jacky did not know of that),
    And told Papa the trick;
He saw him take a slender string,
And round poor Pussy's neck then swing
    A very heavy brick.

His parents being very sad
To find they had a boy so bad,
    To say what was not true,
Determined to correct him then;
And never was he known again
    Such naughty things to do.

Dangerous Sport

POOR PETER was burnt by the poker one day,
    When he made it look pretty and red;
For the beautiful sparks made him think it fine
        play,
    To lift it as high as his head.

But somehow it happen'd, his finger and thumb
    Were terribly scorch'd by the heat;
And he scream'd out aloud for his Mother to come,
    And stamp'd on the floor with his feet.

Now if Peter had minded his Mother's command,
    His fingers would not have been sore;
And he promised again, as she bound up his hand,
    To play with hot pokers no more.

The Chimney Sweeper.

SWEEP! sweep! sweep! sweep! cries little Jack,
With brush and bag upon his back,
    And black from head to foot;
While daily as he goes along,
Sweep! sweep! sweep! sweep! is all his song,
    Beneath his load of soot.

But then he was not always black,
Oh, no! he once was pretty Jack,
    And had a kind Papa;
But, silly child! he ran to play
Too far from home, a long, long way,
    And did not ask Mamma.

So he was lost, and now must creep
Up chimneys, crying, Sweep! sweep! sweep!

49

The Canary.

MARY had a little bird,
　With feathers bright and yellow,
Slender legs,—upon my word,
　He was a pretty fellow !

Sweetest notes he always sung,
　Which much delighted Mary;
Often where his cage was hung,
　She sat to hear Canary.

Crumbs of bread and dainty seeds
　She carried to him daily;
Seeking for the early weeds,
　She deck'd his palace gaily.

This, my little readers, learn,
　And ever practise duly;
Songs and smiles of love return
　To friends who love you truly.

She cried so loud, her mother came
　To ask the reason why;
And said, " Oh, Frances, fie for shame !
　Oh fie ! Oh fie ! Oh fie ! "

But Frances was more naughty still,
　And Betty sadly nipp'd;
Until her mother said, " I will—
　I must have Frances whipp'd."

For, oh, how naughty 'tis to cry,
　But worse, much worse to fight,
Instead of running readily
　And calling out, Good night !

Going to Bed.

THE babe was in the cradle laid,
　And Tom had said his prayers,
When Frances told the nursery-maid
　She would not go up stairs.

Poisonous Fruit.

As Tommy and his sister Jane
Were walking down a shady lane,
They saw some berries, bright and red,
That hung around and overhead.

And soon the bough they bended down,
To make the scarlet fruit their own;
And part they ate, and part in play
They threw about and flung away.

But long they had not been at home
Before poor Jane and little Tom
Were taken, sick and ill, to bed,
And since, I've heard, they both are dead.

Alas ! had Tommy understood
That fruit in lanes is seldom good,
He might have walked with little Jane
Again along the shady lane.

The history of
GILES GINGERBREAD
A LITTLE BOY
Who lived upon learning

CHAP. I.

One day as Gaffer Gingerbread was coming from work, he saw little Giles, who was ragged as a colt, getting up behind Sir Toby Thompson's coach; upon which he called to him: here, Giles, come hither to me. I see, says his father, you want to get upon the coach, but you are climbing at the wrong place, Giles; you should endeavour to get in at the door. Yes, father, said the boy, but that place is not for poor folks. Not for poor folks, replied the father, yes, but it is; a poor man or a poor boy may get a coach if he will endeavour to deserve it. Merit and industry may entitle a man to any thing. Why, Sir Toby, was poor once, yes, as poor as thee, Giles: do not be disheartened, boy, only when you climb, climb in a proper manner, and at the right place, and I will tell you how Sir Toby managed it. But see, the Pig has got out of the sty. Put him in first, and then I will tell you. Giles ran as fast as he could to put in the Pig, for he had learned to do as he was bid, or he would never have made either a good boy or a great man. There is no doing any good for boys and girls who are obstinate, and will not take advice and do as they are bid. No, no! such children never have made great men and women; but are neglected and despised.

CHAP. II.

An Episode; shewing how Sir Toby Thompson became a great man, and obtained so much money, and such a fine coach.

GILES came back puffing and blowing, now father, tell me, now father, tell me, says he, how I may get such a fine coach as Sir Toby's. Ay, says the father, that I will, Giles; I will tell you how Sir Toby got his, and if you behave in the same manner that Sir Toby did, you may get one also, and take up your poor father to ride with you, when he is grown old and weary.
Sir Toby Thompson was the son of Goody

Thompson, and lived at this little Hut upon the Green. His mother was a poor widow, and had three children. Toby was the eldest, and as she was obliged to go out every day to washing, scouring, and such sort of work, she left little Toby at home to take care of his brother and sister, and lead them about.

It happened one day that Goody Thompson had no victuals to leave the children, and they were all crying at the time, when Mr. Goodwill, a rich London tradesman, who had a house in this county, was going by. Bless me, says Mrs. Goodwill, who was with her husband, what is the matter with these poor children, and stepping up to the little one, what do you cry for? said she; I am hungry, answered the child; and I want some bread, cried the other. And what do you cry for? says Mrs. Goodwill to Toby; because I have no bread to give to my brother and sister, says the boy. This is a hard case, says Mrs. Goodwill; I pity the poor children, let us take them home with us and feed them. Ay, with all my heart, says Mr. Goodwill; I pity both

the children and their mother, and I like the biggest boy much; for he who could forget his own wants, and cry for those of his brother and sister, must have a good heart. So for all they were fine folks, Mr. Goodwill took up one child, and Mrs. Goodwill the other, and carried them on, leaving Toby to trot by himself, as you may see.

When the children had a belly full, they no longer cried; but went to play till the evening, when their mother came crying for them, and told Mr. and Mrs. Goodwill her case.

Mr. Goodwill gave her money, and allowed her so much a week, towards the maintenance of herself and children, and took little Toby and sent him to school; where he behaved very well: and soon learnt to read and to write. After some time, Mr. Goodwill took him home to his house in London, to run errands, and do any other business for the servants and clerks in his shop and counting-house.

Now it happened that though Mr. Goodwill was a very honest, charitable, and good man, yet he was not altogether so wise and prudent as one would expect a man to be who lived in London, and knew the world; for he was very fond of horses, frequently went to Newmarket, and other races, and kept two race-horses himself, which ran away with half of the profit of his trade. They were kept at a great expence, turned his thoughts from business, and led him into betting and gaming, which were scandalous. At the time that he was so taken up with his horses, he had the misfortune to have a servant in his house who was not honest; which Toby discovered, and wrote to his master about it, but in a disguised hand, and without putting any name to the letter. Enquiry was made, and money and goods were

missing. Upon which all the servants were examined except Toby, and as he was a boy, and thought incapable of defending himself, the thief laid the robbery on him. Mr. Goodwill, without that consideration which is necessary on these occasions, ordered him immediately to pack up his things, and go about his business. Yes sir, says Toby, crying, but first hear me. I know that you have been defrauded, sir, and I thought it my duty, as you was my master, to inform you of it. I wrote you a letter, sir, in a feigned hand, and without a name, when you was at Newmarket, but at the corner of the letter you will find a private mark, by which you may know it to be mine, and I should not have done this had I been guilty of robbery. No sir, you have been a father to me; and I have been just and honest to you; but this man has not, (pointing to the thief), for I saw him take goods privately out of the warehouse, and carry them to the pawnbrokers. The master was astonished! he looked at the letter, found the mark, and saw the boy was innocent, and then searching the pawnbrokers, the goods were found. Toby knew it was his duty not only to be honest himself, but if possible, to make others so, and you will presently see how God Almighty blessed him for it, and how he was rewarded for his fidelity.

After this, Mr. Goodwill placed great confidence in Toby, and his affairs so prospered, that he became very rich. He then took in Toby as a partner with him, and at his death left him the whole trade, and a large sum of money, which is still increasing; and from being a little ragged boy, and living in the hut, he now rides in his coach.

Think of this, my dear Giles, and learn your book, and say your prayers, and go to church, and be honest, good, and industrious, that you may get a coach also.

CHAP. III.

How little Giles first acquired his learning.

AS soon as Gaffer Gingerbread had finished this story of Sir Toby and his coach, little Giles ran up to his father, and begged that he would give him a book, and teach him to read, that he might become as great a man as Sir Toby Thompson.

Gaffer Gingerbread, who was a pretty good scholar, pulled a book out of his pocket, and

sitting down under a tree with Giles on his lap, now, says he, if you will be a good boy, and mind what I say, you may soon learn to read. You must know, Giles, that all the words in the world are spelt, or made up, of these twenty-four marks or letters, pulling out of his pocket an alphabet cut in pieces, which he had made of gingerbread, for he was by trade a gingerbread baker. These he placed in this manner:

a b c d e f g h i j k l m n o p q r s t u v w x y z

All the words in the world, said Giles, laughing; yes, sirrah, says the father, what do you laugh at? I say all the words in the world; all the words that you and all the people in the world can think on, may be spelt with these letters differently placed. Then let me hear you spell top, said Giles, so you shall, said the father. See here is a *t*, an *o*, and a *p*,—and these placed together make *top*. Ay, that is a little word, says Giles, but you cannot spell plumb-pudding; why, yes, I can, said the father, see here is a *p*, an *l*, a *u*, an *m*, and a *b*, which placed thus, make *plumb*; and here is another *p*, and a *u*, a *d*, and another *d*, an *i*, an *n*, and a *g*, which being placed thus, make *pudding*; these two words put together make *plumb-pudding*.

Let me spell, father, says Giles, and taking the gingerbread letters in his hand, what shall I spell, said he; why, the name of the thing you see, quoth the father, then I'll spell *goose*, says the boy; so saying, he took up a *g*, a *u*, an *f*, and an *e*, and placed them thus, *gufe*; you blockhead, is that your manner of spelling, says the father, who would certainly have been angry, but at this instant, farmer Milton's hog ran at the geese and goslings that were before him, run Giles, run, said the father, away he flew to save the

goslings, which he did with the help of the gander, who laid hold of the hog's ear to keep him off.

See what affection these creatures have for their young, and what care they take of them, what will not a father and mother do to preserve their children; and children ought to do the same to their parents, but they are naughty children who do not consider this, although God Almighty has promised long life to those who do. "Honour thy father and thy mother, that thy days may be long in the land which the Lord thy God giveth thee."

Giles came back crying, (see here he is), and told his father that the geese hissed and laughed at him. Ay, that is because you cannot read, answered the father, come hither, Giles, says he, you must learn to know all the letters, and the sound they have alone, and when joined to others, before you can spell and read. In the word you attempted to spell, you have taken an *f* instead of an *s*, and a *u* instead of *oo*, for want of knowing the letters and their sounds, here take up this A, and look at him well: you see he is very different from the rest. Upon this, Giles took up the letters, and then he read A, A, says he. Ay, Mr. A, I shall know you again, apple for that. B, B, you are not at all like A, Mr. B, I should be a blockhead if I did not know you. C, C, I shall know you Mr. C, indeed, and so will every body that loves custard. D, D, drum and dumpling will make me know you, Mr. D. E, E, eggs and eel-pie for ever. F, F, fine folks and furmity for you, Mr. F. G, G, Gingerbread and gooseberry fool will always make me love you Mr. G. H, H, hog's puddings and hot cockles for ever. I, I, Jack Jones the inkle weaver, will put me in mind of you, Mr. I. K, K, come,

Mr. K, you shall help me to make a kite. L, L, my little lamb and my lark will help me to remember you, Mr. L. M, M, Money for you Mr. M, when I can get it, and when I fool it away, you shall call me monkey. N, N, nuts and Nancy for ever. O, O, oranges, one a penny, two a penny, oranges. P, P, Punch and the puppet show, huzza. Q, Q, you stand for quail, Mr. Q, and I shall always think on you when I see a queer fellow. R, R, you are a raven, Mr. R, and a rat catcher. S, stands for swan. T, T, oh, Mr. T, I know you by my top and trumpet. U, U, Unicorn for that. W, W, a man can never forfeit you when he has a wild duck for dinner. X, X, you look so cross, that I shall know you again by your double face. Y, Y, you are like my yellow hammer, Mr. Y. Z, is a zany, who loves not his book, or his master, or school.

Giles was fond of his book, and as his father gave him a new one every day, which he eat up, it may be truly said he lived upon learning. Sir Toby, hearing what a good boy he was, took him to London in his coach, and no doubt, he will soon get one of his own; when he does, we shall let our readers know it. Farewell.

Giles Gingerbread he lov'd cream, custard and
    curds;
And good books so well, that he eat up his words.

> See here's little Giles,
>   With his Gingerbread book,
> For which he doth long,
>   And at which he doth look;
> Till by longing and looking,
>   He gets it by heart,
> And then he eats it up,
>   As we eat up a tart.

Sixteen Pence is 1^{sh} & 4^d.

The price of this fine flying Toy.

Eighteen Pence is 1^{sh} & 6^d.

This I gave the Negro Boy.

Twenty Pence is 1^s & 8^d.

This in Paper out I laid.

Thirty Pence is 2^{sh} & 6^d.

Which I for a Grammar paid.

Forty Pence is 3^{sh} & 4^d.

This I spent in going to School.

Fifty Pence is 4^{sh} & 2^d.

And with this I bought a rule.

Sixty Pence is just 5^{sh}
Master this in entrance got.

Published by J. Harris, corner of St Pauls, June 1.1818.

Seventy Pence is 5^{sh} & 10^{d}
Who dares say that it is not.

Eighty Pence is 6^{sh} & 8^{d}
This is just a Lawyers fee.

Ninety Pence is 7^{sh} & 6^{d}
Which you all may plainly see.

One Hundred Pence is 8^{sh} & 4^{d}
This I lent to Cousin Ben.

And as he wanted 9^{sh} & 2^{d}
I sent to him the other Ten.

A PRESENT FOR A LITTLE GIRL.

Price One Shilling.

LONDON

Printed and Sold by Wm Darton,
& Jos.^h Harvey
N.º 55 Gracechurch Str.^t
Decr 26.th 1797.

USE no bad words at play, nor play with those who do so. A good girl will do as she is bid; she will not pout with her lips, when she is told to read or spell, but try to do as well as she can. She does not cry over her work, and dir-ty it; but will try to do all neat and clean; and when at her break-fast or tea, she does not cry for rolls or toast, or muf-fins, or crum-pets, when she has got a nice mess of milk and bread. What should we do with-out milk? Cows milk is so good, that some girls and boys live most-ly up-on it. We make cheese and but-ter from milk. Not on-ly cows milk is of great use to men and wo-men, boys and girls; but goats milk is made in-to but-ter and cheese in some places: Even the poor ass gives milk, that is good for the sick. I have been told of a poor man who lost his wife, when their child, a boy, was ve-ry young; and as this man had a she goat, he used to lay the child to the teats of poor Nan-ny, for so he call-ed the goat, and she would let the

boy suck till he fell a-sleep, when the poor man us-ed to put him in a bas-ket, for he had no pro-per cra-dle to rock him in. Nan-ny the goat, was fed well with grass and hay, and her milk fed the lit-tle boy, who grew up to be a tall man. I have read that the man who first built the ci-ty of Rome, where the Pope lives, was fed by the milk of a wolf. I do not say it is not true, but I fear more has been said than is so.

If a girl or boy be cut with a knife, or scratch-ed with a pin, they are sore and in pain; in-deed, some girls cry when they prick their fin-ger with a nee-dle; and if a leg or an arm be broke, they are in sad pain, and can-not sleep; they must lie in bed for a long time, by day and night. Yet some girls will stick a pin in-to a cock-chafer, to make it spin, or pull off the legs of a poor fly for sport. A leg is a leg to a fly as well as to a boy or girl.

Some rude boys had one day got a pigeon which was lame, and its wings be-ing cut it could not fly, so they had tied a string to one of its legs, and put it down to be thrown at with a stick, that he who should knock it down might have it; but just as they were go-ing to throw at it, little Mary ran and begged them to stop, and she would buy the bird. How much, said she, must I give for it? Six-pence, said one of the sad boys. I have but four-pence, said Ma-ry, take all my mo-ney, I do not want the bird, on-ly do not use it ill. How should we like to be thrown at with sticks or stones? Poor birds can feel pain, as boys and girls do, and it is not right to hurt any one of God's creatures; we should use them with mer-cy. There are some men who do not think it right to kill any thing, and feed on-ly on plants and roots, and grain; as rice, wheat, oats, and rye.

Boys like money, so they took Mary's groat, and gave her the poor bird, which she took so much care of, as to cure it of its lame leg, and it fed out of her hand, coo-ed like a dove, and liv-ed a long time in the house. It would be ve-ry plea-sant, if we could now see how cheer-ful the poor bird used to look upon Ma-ry, every morn-ing as she fed it.

Never climb on chairs, they were made to sit on, not to stand upon. See here we have a print of a little girl who did not mind what was said to her, for sometimes she would get upon the window seat, and be in danger of falling out of the window; at other times she would stand upon the fender before the fire, and try to step upon the brass footman, so as to be in danger of setting her frock on fire, or of being scalded by the steam of the boiling water in the tea-kettle.

One day she climbed on the back of the nurse's chair, who, rising up to follow a little boy, that was at play with a dog, the chair fell upon her, and she hurt her head against the floor. "It was well it was no worse," said little Joe, when he heard this story read. "I don't like to climb,"

said Jane, " and it is well that little Ann, we have just heard tell of, did not break some of her bones." What! break her bones with a fall off a chair!" said Tom, " pooh pooh; why there was a schoolboy one day fell out of an apple tree, and did not hurt himself!" " That might happen so, for once," said Joe, " but many a boy has had a leg, a thigh, or an arm broken by climbing." I once heard of a little girl who was much ruder than she should be, and did not always do as she was bid, for one day at breakfast time, she stood upon a leg of the table, and was trying to reach some toast in great haste, instead of asking for it in a proper manner, as she should have done; when the stool slipping from under her feet, she caught hold of the table to save herself from falling, and down fell the urn with the boiling water! She was sadly scalded; her screams were very loud, her pains very great; all this was, for not doing as she had been told. It seems but a little thing to stand on the leg of a table; but doing this caused the little girl to be scalded, to be a long time in pain, and to lie in bed for many days.

Jane was very fond of keeping birds, silkworms, white mice, rabbits, and squirrels; and whilst she attended them with care, her aunt did not forbid it; having told her daily to feed and clean them. One day her aunt found the bird cages dirty, and the glasses very near emptied of their water and feeds. The silkworms were crawling over a parcel of dead leaves, seeking a piece that was moist enough for them to eat. The rabbits were without oats or grains, and were squeaking at the grating of the hutches; her squirrel, for want of food, had got among the tea cups, in search of some biscuits which were kept in the cupboard, and the china was in danger of being broken. Her aunt, as soon as a proper time offered, for she made it a rule not to reprove a child or a

servant whilst any other person was present, told her of the state of the poor animals. This so affected her, that she shed tears, and offered to give the birds and beasts their liberty; but this her aunt would not consent to, well knowing that by being kept a long time in a state of confinement, they were rendered unable to provide for themselves. Jane had been so busy at play with some other little girls in dressing a doll, and riding on the rocking-horse, that she had forgotten her little animals, but ever since, she has daily given her birds and beasts a plenty of food, and kept them clean, as the greatest kindness she could shew them. Thus she suffered pain of mind for not doing as she had been told.

But I have known many a fond mother suffer great pain, for a child not doing as it has been told. When Charles was a little boy, he had leave to play upon the green before the door, and was told not to get over the stile into the field; but after playing for some time, he went to the stile, and saw a horse in the field; he went to play with it, having a stick in his hand; he had been some time in the field before his mother missed him from the door, and fearing he had gone over the stile, she went in search of him, when, to her great surprise, she saw little Charles had got hold of the horse's tail,

playing with the long hairs! She had just time to take him away before he was hurt, and if it had not been a very quiet horse, it might have kicked him to death in a short time.

I knew a little girl, who lived near Kent Road, and one day as a horse stood near her father's door, she was hardy enough to walk with two other girls under its belly more than once; but when the man, to whom the horse belonged, saw what she was doing, he was much afraid, saying, it was a great wonder the horse had not kicked some of them to death; it was a very silly thing, and I hope no child will do so any more.

"Pity the sorrows of a poor old man, who stands in need of help." He is going over a bridge, and at the same time, the wind blows hard enough to blow him down—See, he has lost his hat! I hope some kind man or boy may meet with him, and give him his hat again, to keep his head warm.—I have heard of a man who was blind, that used verses similar to the following.

Good people all, both great and small,
    I'm blind and cannot see;
To my surprise, I lost my eyes
    Beneath a great oak tree.

The thunder dread, crack'd round my head,
    And stunn'd me with affright;
Then quickly came the lightning's flame,
    And made me dark as night.

I have a wife, pride of my life,
    But she is quite in rags;
And babies two, without a shoe,
    Or stocking to their legs.

Good ladies then, and gentlemen,
    I'm poor as any rat,
Your purse don't shut, but kindly put,
    Some money in my hat.

Never stay by the way, when sent to school, and out of sight of your friends.—Mary was the daughter of a farmer, who lived half a mile from the village to which she went to school. When the weather was wet and the paths dirty, she used to carry her dinner with her in a little basket; one day, just as she had entered the village, some idle boys and girls were teasing a goat, and Mary was much pleased at their

whilst another helped her up, screaming and crying for fear. She was not much hurt, but the sight of her dirty frock, stockings and bonnet, reminded her of her dear mother's charge,— *Never to stay and play, when sent to school, or on an errand.*—One of the neighbours, a poor woman, came and took Mary into a cottage, washed her hands and face, and did all she could to clean and comfort her. Being a little composed, she very often thanked the poor woman for her care, and was going to school, when, recollecting her pattens and basket, she went to the place where she had left them, and found a large dog at her dinner, and the bason broke which held her pudding! Fearing she would be late at school, she drove the dog away, put on her pattens, and went with her basket as fast as she could. When she came to the school, her governess perceived she had been crying, and asked her what was the reason. She blushed,

play; she stopped, and joined them in what they called fun: her pattens hindered her from running so fast as she wanted, and her dinner in the basket was an encumberance; therefore she placed both against a wall, and ran towards the goat, calling Bill, Bill, Bill! as the rude boys had done. The goat came towards her faster than she expected, and in trying to escape, she fell: the goat missed her with his horns, but ran upon her with his feet. A great boy at that instant came with a stick and drove him away,

the tears again flowed down her cheeks, and she told all that had passed. The kind teacher, seeing her contrition, was much pleased that Mary had told the truth; saying she hoped this would be a lesson to her in future, not to act contrary to good advice. She not only gave her some dinner, instead of that the dog had eaten, but wrote a note to her parents, commending her candour in telling the truth, and entreated very little blame might be added to the pain Mary had felt for her folly.

INSTRUCTIVE HINTS,

IN EASY LESSONS

FOR CHILDREN.

PART II.

LONDON:

PRINTED BY AND FOR
DARTON AND HARVEY, GRACECHURCH-STREET.

1806.

Price One Shilling.

YOU have fi-nish-ed your book, you say, and want a new les-son.

Ve-ry well. Here it is.

But first, you must go and put a-way care-ful-ly the book you have just read o-ver; that is not to be thrown a-way be-cause you have got a new one. Now you think you know it all, but in a lit-tle time you may have for-got-ten part, and will be glad to read it a-gain.

Be-sides, some of your play-fel-lows may not have such a book, and per-haps they would like to bor-row it of you.

We en-joy a great deal of plea-sure our-selves in giv-ing o-thers plea-sure; and those things which we can-not give, we may, and ought, to lend.

If your book be kept whole, and in its place, you will feel pleasure in thinking, that it is ready when-e-ver you or a-ny body else want it.

O, I can-not find my book, or my hat, &c. is the com-mon com-plaint of ma-ny lit-tle boys and girls; and they run a-bout the house, ma-king a great noise, lo-sing their time, and dis-turb-ing e-ve-ry bo-dy a-round them, be-cause they have not put things in their pro-per places. E-ve-ry time you read you should try to learn some-thing. If you hur-ry through a whole book at one les-son, with-out this, it will do you no good.

If you have now learn-ed to put e-ve-ry thing in its place, and to re-mem-ber where it is, you have learn-ed what will help to make you ea-sy and use-ful through life.

Go, sit down and think up-on this short les-son, " to re-mem-ber a lit-tle, is bet-ter than read-ing a great deal."

You can-not learn too soon, nor re-col-lect too of-ten, that there is a right way and a wrong one, of do-ing e-ve-ry thing: e-ven of hold-ing your nee-dle, fold-ing up your work, and turn-ing over the leaves of your book.

If you learn the right way at first it will soon be ea-sy and plea-sant to you: but if you get the wrong one it will be dif-fi-cult to leave it off.

When you wish to turn o-ver the leaves of

61

your book, do not push them up from the bot-tom with your thumb, this dir-ties and wears them out; but with your fore-fin-ger, just touch the leaf at the top, and it will se-pa-rate from the rest, with-out be-ing spoil-ed.

When you lay a-side your work, it is not to be tum-bled to-ge-ther, and put a-way like a piece of rum-pled pa-per; but it is to be fold-ed up smooth, and put a-way neat-ly; then, when you want it a-gain, it will be much plea-sant-er to see, and much ea-si-er to do.

When your clothes are ta-ken off, they are not to be thrown to-ge-ther in heaps, like so ma-ny old rags, but to be laid smooth and folded up; thus they will keep clean long-er, wear bet-ter and when put on a-gain, they will look much more ti-dy.

Those who will not be care-ful of a stuff gown and a cot-ton a-pron, would not take care of a cot-ton gown, and a mus-lin a-pron.

These you may think are little things, but it is by be-gin-ning to do right in lit-tle things, that we learn to do great ones well.

If it be right to do a thing at all, it is right to do it well; and chil-dren should al-ways be thank-ful to be taught; but if they fan-cy their own way best, they will grow up ob-sti-nate and fool-ish.

It is a great plea-sure to teach chil-dren who are will-ing to learn; and those who do not un-der-stand why they are told to do a thing one way ra-ther than a-nother, should ask the rea-son.

If you wish to learn the best way of doing e-very thing, you may go on im-proving as long as you live; but if not, you may be ig-no-rant until you die.

Come, bring your work, and let me fix it.
What are you making ? A shirt for my fa-ther.

Ve-ry well. He la-bours for you, and you work for him; that is ve-ry right. Sew-ing is a ve-ry use-ful em-ploy-ment; with-out it our cloth-ing would hang loose a-bout us, which would be very trou-ble-some, and it would not keep us so warm. She who sews quick, and well, is like-ly to be a ve-ry use-ful wo-man, and need ne-ver be seen in rags.

The great end of sew-ing is to make us de-cent and com-fort-able, and she is not like-ly to be ei-ther long, who can-not sew.

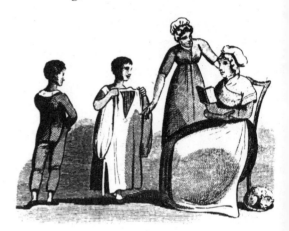

But there is a great deal of sew-ing which is ve-ry use-less, and some which is hurt-ful, as it in-jures the eyes, and con-sumes a great deal of time. Of this sort are fine sam-plers. The co-lours and the verses may be ve-ry good, and the fi-gures and the flow-ers ve-ry gay. But it is ve-ry te-di-ous to do, and ve-ry use-less when done.

In a little time the co-lours will fade, the moths will eat the can-vass, and the poor sampler will be laugh-ed at.

How much better is it to knit stock-ings. Stock-ings are al-ways want-ed: the poor should knit them for them-selves, and the rich may knit them for the poor.

This is work that is al-ways rea-dy. Many peo-ple can knit when they walk, when they read, when their eyes are weak, and some, when they are blind.

Stock-ings which are knit-ted, wear much lon-ger than those which are wo-ven; and no-thing is more cre-dit-a-ble to a lit-tle girl, than to see her with stock-ings of her own knit-ting.

Ma-ny poor chil-dren, who are born blind, help to main-tain them-selves by knit-ting.

Such chil-dren are much hap-pi-er than those who do no-thing that is use-ful.

It is much better to make or mend shirts and shifts, than to work mus-lin; to knit stock-ings, than to or-na-ment sam-plers.

Per-haps, you may have heard sil-ly peo-ple say to chil-dren when they were cry-ing, " if you are not good Tom Dark shall take you."

There is no such per-son as Tom Dark. Go, and shut the win-dow-shut-ters, and the door— now there is no light in the room. We all re-main in our places: the books and the work lie where they did. There is no-thing more, or less, in the room, than there was be-fore.

You re-mem-ber where the spell-ing book lay. Go, and fetch it to me. O, I can-not find it.

Feel a-gain; you know its size, do not bring an-o-ther.

Ve-ry well. This is the book. Go, and o-pen

the shut-ters. Look at it; you did not think you could have found it in the dark.

It is of use to go in-to different pla-ces, to find what we want in the dark; to know the form and the siz-es of things, by feel-ing. Some-times a candle is blown out, by ac-ci-dent; and if we have gone a-bout the house in the dark, we shall be bet-ter a-ble to find what we want, or, at least, can ea-si-ly go back to light it.

Some per-sons, you know, be-come blind. Those who have learn-ed what things are by form and sound, will suf-fer less by such a loss than o-thers.

When your eyes are shut, you can ea-si-ly tell a table from a chair, and a hat from a coat.

You may ea-si-ly try a num-ber of o-ther things, and you will soon learn the dif-fer-ence.

Some blind per-sons can tell the foot-steps of the per-sons they know, and name them from hear-ing them walk.

They can go on er-rands, and on jour-neys, and e-ven serve as guides to tra-vel-lers, through dan-ge-rous ways.

Some can make nets, and whips, and bas-kets; and a great many o-ther use-ful things.

It is only like be-ing in the dark; they can hear, and feel, and taste, and smell, and think; and by u-sing these pow-ers, as well as they can, they are of-ten cheer-ful and hap-py.

Think of this, and you will see that it is ve-ry sil-ly to cry or to be fright-en-ed in the dark. Blind peo-ple are al-ways in the dark, yet they do not cry.

Do you like to see fine sights ?

work so briskly, that the lead broke instantly; she blushed to confess (even so long after) the mean trick of which she was guilty, for immediately she slipped it into the drawer, where it usually lay, and said nothing of the accident.

"It was apprehension of displeasure," said she, "which kept me silent, but I wish, even now, at "this distance of time, that I had gone directly "to my aunt and told her; had she given the "least hint, I should have made my confession; "but, though I felt a desire to have it known, "yet I had not the confidence to go and avow "my giddiness."

"My dear girl, I trust that the compunction "which you felt then, has put you upon your "guard; you saw the fault; you felt its conse-"quences severely, in the reproaches of your "mind. I am confident that you will never err "again in the same way."

"Not for the world, madam; I hid the pencil "in my first surprise, and then, when I recol-"lected how I ought to have acted, had not "courage to retrieve my fault; for so I name "the concealment: breaking the pencil was an "accident."

"You judge well."

"I was betrayed into a second fault by the "inadvertence of speaking too hastily.

"I disliked the taste of asses milk, and having "a very weakly constitution, drank it almost "constantly, so that I was surfeited with it to "such a degree as to nauseate my draught.

"My dear mamma knew my dislike, and "seldom omitted to ask whether I drank all my "milk?

"One day I answered, yes, mamma; but, the "moment I had spoken, recollected, that by mere "chance I spilled a little. I said nothing; but "the disquiet and vexation which I suffered will "ever remain impressed upon my mind; if, by "any accident, my mamma had discovered the "truth, how mean should I have appeared! she "would have suspected that I designed to be "guilty of falsehood, or why did I not immediate-"ly correct it? If the error were involuntary "why did I hesitate to explain the truth to my "dear mamma? Had she been a severe parent "I should have been less culpable; but she "really was the most indulgent, tender, gentle "mother!—Madam, excuse my tears!"

"My dear child, they need no excuse."

Yes, in-deed I do.

Well. I can show you one of the fi-nest it is pos-sible to be-hold.

What is that? Let us go and see it.

Can you get up ve-ry ear-ly in the morn-ing, and go to the top of the hill?

Yes.

Well, if it be fine, then we shall see the sun ri-sing in all his glo-ry; and I scarce-ly know a-ny thing so beau-ti-ful.

Inadvertent Deceit

"Truth is the basis of every virtue."

MISS *Franklin* is a very amiable girl; if she ever happen, through inadvertence, to be guilty of a fault, she comes immediately to me, con-fesses that she has been to blame, and requests my forgiveness.

I was one day applauding her ingenuous tem-per; and she told me, that she had twice in her life suffered much disquiet at two little incidents which might have made her appear deficient in that good quality.

I shall relate them: for, though the things were trifles, trifles discover characters.

The first happened when she was but six years old.

She asked leave to make use of a pencil; and in her joy at obtaining permission, she went to

THE
Tragical Death
OF A
APPLE-PYE,
WHO WAS
Cut in Pieces and Eat by
Twenty Five Gentlemen
WITH WHOM
ALL LITTLE PEOPLE
OUGHT
To be very well acquainted)

Printed by John Evans,
42, Long-lane, West-smithfield, London

A Apple Pye

B Bit it

C Cut it

D Dealt it

E Eat it

F Fought for it

G Got it

H Had it

J Join'd for it

K Kept it

L Long'd for it

M Mourn'd for it

N Nodded at it

O Open'd it

P Peep'd in it

Q Quarter'd it

R Run for it

S Stole it

T Took it

V View'd it

W Wanted it

X, Y, Z, and &, they all
wish'd for a piece in
hand.

At last they every one agreed,
Upon the Apple Pye to feed;
But as there seem'd to be so
many,
Those who were last might not
have any,

Unless some method there was
taken,
That every one might save
their bacon,

They all agreed to stand in
order
Round the Apple Pye's fine
border;
Take turn as they in hornbook
stand,
From great A, down to &,
In equal parts the pye divide,
As you may see on t'other side.

A CURIOUS
DISCOURSE
That passed between the
TWENTY FIVE LETTERS
AT
DINNER-TIME.

A 1.
Says A, give me a good large
slice.

B 2.
Says B, A little, bit but nice.

C 3.
Says C, Cut me a piece of crust.

D 4.
Says D, It is as dry as dust.

E 5.
Says E, I'll eat now fast who will

F 6.
Says F, I vow I'll have my fill.

G 7.
Says G, give it to me good
and great.

H 8.
Says H, A little bit I hate.

I 9.
Says I, I love the juice the best

K 10.
And K the very same confess'd

L 11.
Says L, There's nothing more
I love.

M 12.
Says M, It makes your teeth
to move.

N 13.
N notic'd what the others said

O 14.
O others plates with grief sur
vey'd.

P 15.
P prais'd the cook up to the life

Q 16.
Q quarrel'd 'cause he'd a bad
knife.

R 17.
Says R, It runs short I'm afraid

S 18.
S silent sat and nothing said.

T 19.
T thought that talking might
lose time.

U 20.
U understood it at meals a
crime

W 21.
W wished there had been a
quince in;

X 22.
Says X, Those cooks there'
no convincing.

Y 23.
Says Y, I'll eat, let other's wish

Z 24.
Z sat as mute as any fish,

& 25.
While & he lick'd the dish.

Having concluded their dis-
courses, and dinner together, I
have nothing more to add, but
that if my little readers are
pleased with what they have
found in this book, they have
nothing to do but to run to Mr.
Evans's, No. 42, Long-lane,
West-Smithfield, where they
may have several books, not
less entertaining than this, of
of the same size and price.

But that you may not think
I leave you too abruptly, I here
present you with the picture of
the old woman who made the

Apple Pye you have been reading about, she has several more
in her basket, and she promised
if you are good children, you
shall never go supperless to bed
while she has one left. But as
good people always ask a blessing of God before meals, therefore, as a token that you are
good and deserve a pye, you
must learn the two following
Graces, the one to be said before your meals the other after.
And the Lord's prayer every
night and morning.

THE KNIFE-GRINDER'S BUDGET.

Old Billy, poor man !
Is depriv'd of his sight,
But still with his music
Produces delight.

PRICE ONE-PENNY.

The Huxter and Donkey
Are both on their legs :
They're going to market
For butter and eggs.

"Come buy my fine Ap-
ples,"
The old Woman cries,
"You cannot have better
"For eating or pies."

Here comes for the Butcher
A fine lusty Calf,
For the killing of which
He perhaps will get half.

"Be quick as a Lamp-
lighter !"
Sometimes we say :
Here's one upon duty
Fast tripping away.

Poor Ned, I'm afraid,
Cannot meet with h[is]
horse ;
He seems quite distracted
At so great a loss.

You see the old Laundress
At work in her drills ;
But I fear she's too old
To crimp you your frills.

Come buy my fat Rabbits,
Come, Ladies, and buy;
With mutton they make
A most excellent pie.

You here see a poor ma[n]
Repairing a chair ;
He sits on the ground,
Quite expos'd to the ai[r]

uy a good sweeping-
   brush,—
"Hand-brushes buy,—
ll sell you cheap brush-
   es,"—
The old man doth cry.

Poor Jack ! I'm afraid
   That thy bum will be
   sore :
That footmen were boot-
   jacks
   I ne'er knew before.

When the Hen calls her
   Chickens,
   They follow straight-
   way ;
So Children should always
   Their Parents obey.

e Child and Miss Pussy
Do play very nice ;
t Pussy had much rather
Play with some mice.

The Girl you see swing-
   ing,
   If the band only break,
Will be in great danger
   Of breaking her neck.

This Lady of pleasure
   Is taking fresh air ;
Which may do very well
   If the weather keep fair

Keeper ! thy visage
Is dreadful indeed !
y presence I'll flee
With all possible speed.

A Bull-baiting now
   Puts an end to my book :
The scene is so cruel,
   I can scarce bear to
   look.

THE
KNIFE-GRINDER'S
BUDGET.

"Swing-up, my Lads !"
   The Drill-Sergeant cries,
"And fix on the Fugle-man
"Each of your eyes."

PRICE ONE PENNY.

THE HISTORY OF

SAM,

THE SPORTSMAN,

AND HIS GUN,

ALSO, OF

HIS WIFE JOAN.

YORK:

Printed and Sold by J. Kendrew, Colliergate.

There was a little man,
And he had a little gun,
    And he liv'd by the side of a wood ;
He had a little wife,
Who lov'd him as her life,
    And to please him would do what she could.

He took up his little gun.
With which he oft made fun
    By shooting at the birds in the ai
So he went into the wood,
As he thought 'twould do him goo
    For he lov'd of his health to ta
        care.

When to the wood he came,
He prepar'd to take his aim
    With his bullets which were made of lead ;
For two birds he then did see,
As they sat upon a tree,
    And before you'd say bo, they were dead.

Then he went to the brook,
And so sly he there did look,
    That you'd think he intended to fish ;
But such a taste had he,
That he rather lov'd to see,
    On his table a duck on a dish.

But his loving wife so neat,
Had a little bit of meat,
    Which she meant to be boil'd the pot ;
And so unto him did say,
This will serve another day,
    As we a good dinner now have g

Then as soon as he had din'd
It came into his mind,
    To take his gun again to the lake ;
For since he had such luck,
To shoot the little duck,
    He would go try to bring home the drake.

Now the duck was in his eye,
Says he, I'm sure I'll try,
    While you swim their so meek and so mild.
To shoot you in the head,
And directly it was dead,
    But it quack'd as though it was wild.

He then did take it home,
And gave it to his Joan,
    And told her to dress it very ni
But, says he, you must take care,
And of burning it beware,
    And make me a pudding of rice.

One son this queer pair had,
And a very fine lad,
    His name it was little Tom Tucker,
And I dare to say,
Before this very day,
    You've heard that he sung for his supper.

Now when she'd got it drest,
'Twas a delicate feast,
    For Sam and his sweet loving wife,
The bones they did pick,
And their lips they did lick,
    And they eat it without any strife.

So you know all the fun,
Of Sam and his gun,
    Also of Tom and his mother ;
As you have read it o'er,
You need do so no more,
    But go to the shop for some othe

The Book of Games

THOMAS WHITE was the only son of a gentleman of fortune, in the neighbourhood of London. Mr. White had four daughters, but Thomas was his only son; two of his sisters were much older, and the others considerably younger than himself. Little Tom, it may easily be supposed, was a great favourite; indeed his uniform sweetness of temper, and the excellence of his disposition, could not fail endearing him to all who knew him.

As Mr. White was not engaged in business, he devoted a large portion of his time to the education of his son; an employment in which he found so much pleasure, that he formed the plan of keeping Tom, who was both diligent and tractable, at home, and bringing him up himself.

Tom was not deficient in abilities; it may therefore be supposed, that under an instructor so able, and so indefatigable, he made considerable progress; and when he was ten years old, he was certainly much forwarder than the generality of boys at his age. Mr. White, delighted with his son's improvement, found that the task of instructing him daily became more pleasing; but he was prevented finishing the work he had begun, and completing his education, by the sudden death of a friend on the Continent, to settle whose affairs he was obliged to take a journey into Russia; and he determined to place Tom at some good school during his absence.

Dr. Benson, a respectable clergyman, with whom he had long been acquainted, was the person to whose care Mr. White determined to consign his son. The residence of this gentleman was at a pleasant village in Sussex, a few miles from the coast. Dr. Benson had three sons, the eldest was soon to take orders, the second was about fifteen, and George, the youngest, was not quite eleven. In the care of his parish, and the education of his sons, the doctor was indefatigable; but as they were of different ages, he found that his time would admit of more employment, and he had for many years taken a limited number of pupils. He had at present a vacancy for one, and willingly consented to receive the son of his old friend.

Tom White did not hear that it was necessary for him to leave home without experiencing a severe degree of regret. Warmly attached to the friends with whom he had so happily passed his life, it is not to be wondered that he should feel much distressed at leaving them; but convinced that his father would not have determined to part with him, if he had not thought it necessary, he did not offer to oppose his wishes.

As Mr. White was anxious to accompany his son himself, before he quitted England, he hastened as much as possible his departure; and in little more than a week, from his first hearing his father's intentions, he was received into the family of the respectable Dr. Benson.

It was on the second of May, that Thomas White, for the first time in his life, quitted his fond parents' roof, and with his father set forward in a post-chaise for the delightful village which was for some time to be his residence.

It is needless to describe a parting, which, it will easily be believed, occasioned to all parties the most lively regret. In bidding adieu to his mother and sisters, Thomas experienced a degree

of sorrow he had never known before, nor was their distress less than his own. He, however, supported the painful separation with great courage, and it was not till he was seated by his father, and had lost sight of the house, and all that it contained, that he permitted himself to give way to his long suppressed feelings; but then, unable to restrain his tears, he threw himself back in the chaise, and for a few minutes gave vent to those expressions of sorrow which he had hitherto with the utmost difficulty endeavoured to prevent.

His father, who had admired the fortitude with which he had supported this distressing separation, doubted not that he would soon recover himself, and took no notice of him. He was not mistaken; in less than a quarter of an hour, Thomas had, by a laudable exertion, gained sufficient composure to enter into conversation with his father.

Pleased with this instance of self-command, Mr. White endeavoured all in his power to render the ride agreeable; he made him remark the beauties of the surrounding country; told him some anecdotes relating to the towns they passed through, and the gentlemen's seats they saw at a distance.

HOCKEY.

As they could not immediately procure fresh

horses at one of the places they stopped at, Mr. White, with a view of diverting his son, proposed taking a little walk, to which Thomas readily consented. After they had walked for some time in a path which skirted a wood, they came to an open place, where some well looking boys were at play. Each of them had a sort of hooked stick, with which they were beating a ball. Thomas stood for some time looking at them, and then asked his father what game they were playing at.

Mr. White.—It is called Hockey. Those boys seem to play well; but I cannot say it is an amusement of which I am very fond.

Thomas.—Why not, sir? it seems a very pretty game.

Mr. White.—I cannot help thinking it a rather dangerous one; though I believe it is, in reality, not more so than many others; it was a favourite amusement among us, when I was a boy at school, but it was put a stop to by a very melancholy accident.

Thomas.—Pray sir, what was that?

Mr. White.—You have heard me speak of a boy I was particularly fond of, James Robson.

Thomas.—O yes, often; he is the one who is Captain Robson now, is he not? the gentleman who dined at our house one day last Christmas, and who has only one eye?

Mr. White.—The same; and he lost his eye playing at Hockey.

Thomas—Dear, did he? Did you knock it out, for I have heard you say you always played together?

Mr. White.—No, fortunately, I did not. A boy who had not been long at the school, and to whom Robson was teaching the game, in striking at the ball, missed his aim, and gave him so severe a blow, as to occasion the loss of his eye.

Thomas.—O how unhappy the poor boy must have been who did it!

Mr. White.—Indeed I believe he was, for he was a good boy, and very fond of Robson.

Thomas.—Was it long before it got well, pray sir?

Mr. White.—Yes a great while, and he had nearly lost the sight of the other eye, in consequence of the violent inflammation which the pain occasioned. This accident banished Hockey altogether from the school, and I have never liked the thoughts of the game, from that time to this.

THE LETTER.

Dear Father,

As you told me I might write to you soon, I am now going to begin a letter; I hope you will receive it before you leave England.

You told me, sir, that I should be happy here, and that I should like Doctor Benson; and I am sure you will be glad to hear that you were not mistaken. I do like him very much indeed; he is so kind, and so gentle; and as for George, I quite love him already; he is as good tempered as his father; and so lively, and sensible too.

I am sure you will be glad to hear that the Doctor does not think me more backward in my education than those boys who are of my own age. I am afraid you will call me very *vain*, but I do not think George Benson seems much forwarder than I am. But, dear sir, this is not the case at play. Do you know I can hardly play at all, or at least I could not when I came here. But I have made great improvement since then. I have played at trap-ball, and I have learned all the leaping games; and I can take the leap in height and the leap in length now.

The Doctor has had a swing put up in the garden, between the two walnut-trees; and very pleasant we find it, when we have made ourselves warm with leaping, to go under their shade and swing. Mr. Edward Benson was sitting at the parlor window, the other morning, and he drew a sketch of the swing, and two or three of us with it; and as I thought you would like to see it, I have tried to copy it, as well as I could, to send to you. Mr. Edward said, that he meant the one in the swing for me, and the other two for his brothers; and I think that in his drawing there is some resemblance; but I am afraid you will not find much in mine.

George Benson is come to tell me, that if I want my letter to go to day, I must leave off directly, or it will be too late for the post; but I cannot finish it, without begging you to write to me very soon, as I do much want to hear from you. Good bye, my dear father, give my love to my mother and sisters, and believe me to be

Your dutiful and affectionate son,

THOMAS WHITE.

FOOT-BALL.

" WHAT shall we do with ourselves ? " was an enquiry made by two or three of the boys, one day, when they came out of the school-room.

" O, I will tell you," cried George Benson, as he ran into the field. " I have just been out with my brother, and I have brought home a new toy, and I am sure none of you can guess what it is."

" If you are sure of that, you may as well tell us at once, I think," said James.

George Benson.—We stopped at Mr. Wigton's, and he has lately been to London, and he brought some playthings down for his children, and among the rest a fine large foot-ball. One of them, however, contrived to send it through the dining-room window, so their mother thinks it is not a proper toy for them, and so she gave it to me to kick about the field, for it can do no mischief there she says. Look what a nice one it is.

James Benson.—A nice one, indeed. Do you know how to play with it ?

George Benson.—Not I, indeed, but I think we may invent a game for ourselves.

James.—What sort of a game can you make ?

George.—First, I think, we will divide ourselves into two parties. How many are there of us ?

White.—Only four. Jackson and Price are gone into the town.

George.—Well then we shall be two on a side. You, White, shall be along with me. Now I will kick the ball with all my force, and one of you must try to strike it with your foot and return it to us. Either White or I must be ready to send it back again. When either party misses the ball when it comes to be their turn to strike, their opponent must reckon one. We may make the game eleven, or more if you like it better.

James Benson.—I think you have contrived a very good game, George, so let us begin.

" Well done, well done," cried George, as James Benson received the ball with his foot, and sent it to a considerable distance. White watched the direction it took, and was ready to return it, and it travelled several times from one party to the other, before it fell to the ground.

" Now, do not you think," said George, " this is a famous good game ? There is so much exercise in it, it makes me warm, even such a day as this."

The young folks continued to enjoy their new mode of diversion, till White was summoned to the parlour. I shall not attempt to describe his mingled astonishment and joy, when on opening the door he saw his father. If any of my young readers have ever unexpectedly seen a beloved parent, after many months separation, they will be able to form some idea of the sensations of the delighted boy.

After some conversation Mr. White informed his son, that he had landed at Dover the preceding day, and that as he thought the meeting with his family would be doubly pleasant, if they could all enjoy it together, he had determined to travel along the coast to Kingston, and as the holidays were so near take him home with him. " It will not make much difference," continued he, "and as the accounts Dr. Benson has given me of your attention and assiduity, are such as I could wish for, I am happy in being able to reward your obedience to my parting injunctions.

"The chaise will be here in a few minutes, so go and take leave of your school-fellows, and tell your friend George, we shall expect his company at Clapham, for part of the holidays."

The business of taking leave was soon over. Thomas bid adieu to Dr. Benson and his young friends, and stepped into the chaise with his father, without finding his pleasure at going home at all lessened, by the thoughts that in a few weeks he should return again to the KINGSTON ACADEMY.

The
Talking Bird
or
Dame Trudge
and her
Parrot

THE PROMISE

1. Now Old Goody Trudge with her parrot began
To lay down a simple, but excellent plan,
  By which they might still be together :
"Whene'er," said the dame, " I on visiting go,
Perch'd safe on my shoulder, my Poll shall go too,
  Provided it be not bad weather."

INTRODUCTION

Of old Goody Trudge and her talkative bird,
My juvenile friends may have probably heard,
  Or seen some account of at least :
But lest you should not, I'll attempt in my verse,
Her whimsical oddities now to rehearse ;
  For sure they'll afford you a feast.

PREPARATIONS FOR VISITING

The promise was made with a view to be kept :
The dame and her parrot both heartily slept,
  And soon in the morning awoke.
" Today," said the Goody, " my Poll shall take
    tea
With old neighbour All-gossip, where we shall see
  Or hear of some subject for joke."

THE GIFT

Dame Trudge had a brother, a rover was he,
Who quitted his country, fam'd India to see ;
  And on his return he thus sung :—
"Think not, my dear sister, I'm laden with pelf,
But thank your kind stars that I've brought back
    myself,
  And brought you a bird with a *tongue*."

ARRIVAL AT MISS ALL-GOSSIP'S

The swift circling moments flew merrily round ;
The visitors went—and a parrot they found
  On the top of Miss All-gossip's head.
Dame Trudge paid her compliments, sat herself
    down
Her parrot flew up to the side of her crown,
  And listen'd to all that was said.

THANKS

"O lovely ! O charming ! " his sister exclaim'd,
I've often been told the East Indies were fam'd
  For birds that could chatter and sing :
My brother ! you now have approv'd yourself kind,
For this is a gift so exact to my mind,
  'Tis just the identical thing."

SCANDAL

Miss All-gossip talk'd, to be sure, as her tongue
Had been upon wires most tastefully hung,
  And freely anointed with oil ;
The *ladies* afforded her ample employ—
She cut up their persons and dresses with joy,
  And cruelly laugh'd o'er the spoil.

1

2

3

4

5

6

7

10

8

11

9

12

DANGER OF BEING TALKATIVE

2. " My dear ! " said our Poll to Miss All-gossip's
    bird,
  " Pray tell me, if ever so much you have heard
    Of your mistress, what *gentlemen* say ? "
  " A *Venus !* " the humorous creature replied—
  "Aye, aye " said the other ; " but truth may be
    tried,
    When *beauty* shall vanish away."

OFFENCE

A wound may be given, though aim'd in the dark—
Miss All-gossip felt the intended remark ;
  She knew she to *fibbing* was prone :—
Her countenance fell, and her anger was fir'd,
The tea was remov'd, and the guests soon retir'd,
  To leave the poor lady alone.

DANCING

. A few days elaps'd, Goody Trudge was amaz'd,
And, trust me, young reader, as equally pleas'd,
  When Puss and her parrot she found
A minuet performing with excellent grace,
Which—had it but been in a suitable place—
  With shouts of applause had been crown'd.

A CONCERT

. A dance and a concert were afterwards plann'd,
Puss play'd on the fiddle, though not with a hand,
  She did quite as well with her paw :
Poll sung by the notes, while Pug on the ground,
Both footed with spirit and turn'd himself round,
  As neatly as ever you saw.

QUARRELLING

But after this sport, a sad quarrel occurr'd
Between Goody's magpie, and Poll, her best bird,
  Which caus'd much ill language and rage :
The old lady's temper was now so much try'd,
She scolded them both, and she beat them beside,
  And fasten'd them each in their cage.

SYMPTOMS OF GOOD CONDUCT

6. The punishment over, and pardon receiv'd,
  Our parrot contriv'd her good name to retrieve,
    By reading, when weather prov'd wet,
  A lecture on heads, replete with true fun ;
  Then next, as a governess, school she begun,
7. And read to her Dame the Gazette.

FURTHER ECCENTRICITIES

8. Dame Trudge's militia this parrot review'd,
  And (hiding her mistress's work) she pursu'd
    A plan she had form'd by the bye :—
  The fortunes of all her companions she told,
  How some should be punish'd for being too bold,
    And some should old bachelors die.

DISASTER AT MARKET

9. When Poll, Pug and Puss, Squirrel, Mag, and
    the Dame,
  In solemn procession to market all came ;
    It sure was a laughable sight !
10. But when the great dog made his dreadful
    attack,
  And a quarrel ensu'd as the party came back,
    O there was a terrible fight !

POLL TURNED COUNSELLOR

11. Victorious at length, and return'd from the
    town,
  See Poll, in her counsellor's wig, band, and gown,
    Most solemnly reading a brief !
  But sorry I am my young readers to tell,
  That Poll, who could read and could argue so well,
    Should at last prove a bit of a thief.

INGRATITUDE

12. 'Tis shocking, most shocking, but surely too
    true—
  Away with her Goody's best bonnet she flew,
    Nor could be persuaded to stop.
  If by chance her adventures should ere come to
    light,
  The whole of the tale I'll immediately write,
    And you'll get it at HARRIS's shop.

Peter Piper's Practical Principles of Plain and Perfect Pronunciation

PETER PIPER'S POLITE PREFACE.

PETER PIPER Puts Pen to Paper, to Produce his Peerless Production, Proudly Presuming it will Please Princes, Peers, and Parliaments, and Procure him the Praise and Plaudits of their Progeny and POSTERITY, as he can prove it Positively to be a PARAGON, or Playful, Palatable, Proverbial, Panegyrical, Philosophical, Philanthropical Phænomenon of Productions.

B b

Billy Button bought a butter'd Biscuit:
Did Billy Button buy a butter'd Biscuit?
If Billy Button bought a butter'd Biscuit,
Where's the butter'd Biscuit Billy Button bought?

A a

ANDREW Airpump ask'd his Aunt her Ailment:
Did Andrew Airpump ask his Aunt her Ailment?
If Andrew Airpump ask'd his Aunt her Ailment,
Where was the Ailment of Andrew Airpump's Aunt?

C c

Captain Crackskull crack'd a Catchpoll's Cockscomb:
Did Captain Crackskull crack a Catchpoll's Cockscomb?
If Captain Crackskull crack'd a Catchpoll's Cockscomb,
Where's the Catchpoll's Cockscomb Captain Crackskull crack'd?

D d

F f

Davy Dolldrum dream'd he drove a Dragon:
Did Davy Dolldrum dream he drove a Dragon?
If Davy Dolldrum dream'd he drove a Dragon,
Where's the Dragon Davy Dolldrum dream'd he
    drove?

Francis Fribble figur'd on a Frenchman's Filly:
Did Francis Fribble figure on a Frenchman's
    Filly?
If Francis Fribble figur'd on a Frenchman's Filly,
Where's the Frenchman's Filly Francis Fribble
    figur'd on?

E e

G g

Enoch Elkrig ate an empty Eggshell:
Did Enoch Elkrig eat an empty Eggshell?
If Enoch Elkrig ate an empty Eggshell,
Where's the empty Eggshell Enoch Elkrig ate?

Gaffer Gilpin got a Goose and Gander:
Did Gaffer Gilpin get a Goose and Gander?
If Gaffer Gilpin got a Goose and Gander,
Where's the Goose and Gander Gaffer Gilpin got?

H h

Humphrey Hunchback had a Hundred Hedgehogs:
Did Humphrey Hunchback have a Hundred
    Hedgehogs?
If Humphrey Hunchback had a Hundred Hedge-
    hogs,
Where's the Hundred Hedgehogs Humphrey
    Hunchback had?

J j

Jumping Jacky jeer'd a jesting Juggler:
Did Jumping Jacky jeer a jesting Juggler?
If Jumping Jacky jeer'd a jesting Juggler,
Where's the jesting Juggler Jumping Jacky
    jeer'd?

I i

Inigo Impey itch'd for an Indian Image:
Did Inigo Impey itch for an Indian Image?
If Inigo Impey itch'd for an Indian Image,
Where's the Indian Image Inigo Impey itch'd for?

K k

Kimbo Kemble kick'd his Kinsman's Kettle:
Did Kimbo Kemble kick his Kinsman's Kettle?
If Kimbo Kemble kick'd his Kinsman's Kettle,
Where's the Kinsman's Kettle Kimbo Kemble
    kick'd?

L l

Lanky Lawrence lost his Lass and Lobster:
Did Lanky Lawrence lose his Lass and Lobster?
If Lanky Lawrence lost his Lass and Lobster,
Where are the Lass and Lobster Lanky Lawrence
    lost?

N n

Neddy Noodle nipp'd his Neighbour's Nutmegs:
Did Neddy Noodle nip his Neighbour's Nutmegs?
If Neddy Noodle nipp'd his Neighbour's Nutmegs,
Where are the Neighbour's Nutmegs Neddy
    Noodle nipp'd?

M m

Matthew Mendlegs miss'd a mangled Monkey:
Did Matthew Mendlegs miss a mangled Monkey,
If Matthew Mendlegs miss'd a mangled Monkey?
Where's the mangled Monkey Matthew Mend-
    legs miss'd?

O o

Oliver Oglethorpe ogled an Owl and Oyster:
Did Oliver Oglethorpe ogle an Owl and Oyster?
If Oliver Oglethorpe ogled an Owl and Oyster,
Where are the Owl and Oyster Oliver Oglethorpe
    ogled?

P p

Peter Piper pick'd a Peck of Pepper:
Did Peter Piper pick a Peck of Pepper ?
If Peter Piper pick'd a Peck of Pepper,
Where's the Peck of Pepper Peter Piper pick'd ?

R r

Rory Rumpus rode a raw-boned Racer:
Did Rory Rumpus ride a raw-bon'd Racer ?
If Rory Rumpus rode a raw-bon'd Racer,
Where's the raw-bon'd Racer Rory Rumpus rode?

Q q

Quixote Quicksight quiz'd a queerish Quidbox:
Did Quixote Quicksight quiz a queerish Quidbox?
If Quixote Quicksight quiz'd a queerish Quidbox,
Where's the queerish Quidbox Quixote Quick-
    sight quiz'd ?

S s

Sammy Smellie smelt a Smell of Smallcoal:
Did Sammy Smellie smell a Smell of Smallcoal ?
If Sammy Smellie smelt a Smell of Smallcoal,
Where's the Smell of Smallcoal Sammy Smellie
    smelt ?

T t

Tip-Toe Tommy turn'd a Turk for Two-pence:
Did Tip-Toe Tommy turn a Turk for Two-pence?
If Tip-Toe Tommy turn'd a Turk for Two-pence,
Where's the Turk for Two-pence Tip-Toe
    Tommy turn'd ?

U u

Uncle's Usher urg'd an ugly Urchin:
Did Uncle's Usher urge an ugly Urchin ?
If Uncle's Usher urg'd an ugly Urchin,
Where's the ugly Urchin Uncle's Usher urg'd ?

V v

Villiam Veedon vip'd his Vig and Vaistcoat:
Did Villiam Veedon vipe his Vig and Vaistcoat ?
If Villiam Veedon vip'd his Vig and Vaistcoat,
Where are the Vig and Vaistcoat Villiam Veedon
    vip'd ?

W w

Walter Waddle won a walking Wager:
Did Walter Waddle win a walking Wager ?
If Walter Waddle won a walking Wager,
Where's the walking Wager Walter Waddle
    won ?

X x Y y Z z

X Y Z have made my Brains to crack-o,
X smokes, Y snuffs, and Z chews tobacco;
Yet oft by XYZ much learning's taught;
But Peter Piper beats them all to nought.

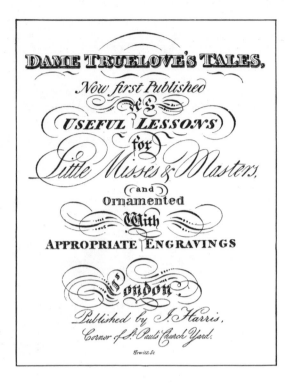

DAME TRUELOVE'S TALES,

Now first Published

USEFUL LESSONS

for

Little Misses & Masters,

and

Ornamented

With

APPROPRIATE ENGRAVINGS

London

Published by J. Harris,
Corner of St Pauls Church Yard.

Hewitt Sc

CHARLES.

CHARLES was a fine boy of four years of age; his cheeks were like two red apples, for he spent great part of the day in the garden, running about and rolling on the grass; that is, from seven o'clock in the morning till twelve, at which time his Grandpapa was ready to receive him, and not sooner. The moment the clock struck that hour, away he ran, and bounced into the room where he knew he was always welcome; and the old gentleman calling him to sit upon his knee, usually asked what he had been doing, and whether he had learnt his lesson. Charles was not very fond of his book, and his Grandpapa often told him that if he did not learn to read, when he grew up, he would be called Sir Charles Dunce, and all the boys in the town would laugh at him; but he did not mind it much, he only kissed his Grandpapa, and said he would learn his lesson when he could find time. One day he entered the room, saying he was very unhappy indeed, and taking his seat upon his Grandpapa's knee, told him that little Johnny Gibson had got a jacket and trowsers, whilst he was kept like a girl in petticoats; and that he thought it was very hard upon him, " a great boy as I am," said he, " more than four years old; there is my sister Maria always calling me. *Miss Charley*, a little

thing like her, no bigger than my thumb ! "—

" Indeed, Charles, it is a very sad thing," said his Grandpapa, " but I must tell you that it is your own fault; John Gibson can read little Tales, and Dialogues in words of one syllable, and has had his jacket and trowsers as a reward for his attention to his learning, whilst you are so idle that you scarcely know your letters; you must therefore content yourself with your petticoats for some time longer."

Charles was much ashamed and hung down his head for some minutes, but from that time he learnt his lesson every day, and never went to run in the garden till he had done it, so that in a few months he had the pleasure of seeing himself dressed in a jacket and trowsers, and equal in all respects to John Gibson, and every other boy of his age.

THE BALLOON.

" OH Harry, Harry ! pray come here," cried Harriet G. to her brother, who was gathering wild flowers at a little distance, to make a nosegay for her, " do pray come, and tell me what that great thing is which I see in the sky."

Harry ran directly to see the strange sight, but he laughed as he ran towards her, because he thought it could be nothing but a cloud; he had often seen clouds very oddly shaped, sometimes like little boys and girls, sometimes like trees and houses, for he was a very clever little boy, observed every thing, and liked to be told the meaning of what he saw.

With all his cleverness, however, Master Harry was very much surprised when his sister

pointed at a great round thing mounting in the air, with something hanging at the lower part of it, just like their Papa's boat, which was kept in the boat house near the river. " What can it be, Harriet ? " said he, " it makes me think of a picture in one of my little books, where there is a great monstrous bird flying away with a poor lamb—but look ! look !—there are two men in that thing like a boat—oh dear ! and flags ! "—

" I am frightened," said little Harriet, getting close to her brother, who was two years older than herself—" suppose it were to fall down upon us, boat and men and all, we should be killed, Harry !—but here comes old Giles, perhaps he can tell us what sort of creature it is, which is flying away with the two poor men."

They went up to Giles directly, but he could only tell them that the strange thing was called a Balloon, and that the men in the boat were two very clever gentlemen, who had found out the way to make the Balloon go up to the clouds, and even to pass through them. " How it is done," added he, " I am but a poor labourer, and as you may suppose, not learned enough to be able to tell you, nor would you perhaps understand me if I could, but your Papa will explain it to you when you are older; all that I can say is, that if my father had had money to put me to school, I do not think it would have been thrown away, for I dearly love books, Master Harry, but alack-a-day, I have no time for reading.

" I have no doubt that the two gentlemen gone up with the Balloon, when they were little boys like you, spent the greatest part of their time in learning their lessons, and reading such books as were given to them; and so they got on from little books to large ones, till they grew up to be young men, and then they found out this wonderful way of paying a visit to the clouds. Who knows, Master Harry, if you are not an idle young gentleman, but mind your lessons rather than spend all your time in play—who knows, I say, what wonderful things you may one day find out."

Harry was much delighted at the thought of being a man of learning, and as the Balloon was now out of sight, ran home to his Papa to ask a dozen or two of questions; and little Harriet was glad the *great creature* was gone, for she could not help being afraid that it would fall upon her head.

LITTLE LAURA.

THERE was once a little girl who lived with her mother in a house by the road side; it was a very pretty house, and it had a flower garden before it, and an apple orchard on one side, and a poultry yard and a dairy on the other. This little girl was called Laura, and she was a very good child, obedient to her parents, and good-natured and kind to her neighbours and acquaintances, so that every body loved and were glad to see her at their houses; but where she spent the most of her time was at the house of an old lady who had taken a great liking to her, because she behaved so properly at church, where, instead of gaping round, and standing on tip-toe to peep into the pews, as many children do, without thinking of the place they are in, she minded nothing but the clergyman; and as she had been taught to know when to kneel and when to stand up, she never neglected to do so at the proper time. She often went to breakfast with this old lady, and spent the whole day with her; and there was a pretty little summer-house in the garden, and she had it nicely furnished with a little table and two or three green

Caroline

Jane Primrose

chairs, and a green blind to shade it from the sun, and it was called Laura's own parlour, and Mr. and Mrs. Martin (that was the lady's name) ordered her tea-table to be taken into the summer-house one fine afternoon, and told Laura she intended to drink tea with her; so Laura was mistress of the tea-table that day, and poured out the tea, and helped her friend to some cake and bread and butter, and was as happy as a queen.

In the Winter she had a scarlet cloak and bonnet, which made her look something like little Red Riding-Hood, and she went to see Mrs. Martin almost every day, for though she could not be so well amused as in Summer, she

Dangers of Swinging

never neglected her good friend who was so kind to her; and if she happened to be unwell, either stayed with her to ring her bell when she wanted any thing, and sit by her side, or went two or three times a day to know if she were better.

Thus the little Laura was the happiest child in the world, and all children may be happy if they follow her example.

EMILY HAYWOOD.

EMILY Haywood was a great reader, though but a little girl; she was very young when she learned to read, but she was fond of it, and people do best what they are most fond of; her cousin Charlotte was a year and a half older than she was, and some people thought her a very clever child, for she could throw her skipping rope over her head and over her shoulders, and

cross it in many ways which I cannot describe, for I am an old woman and know nothing about skipping; but this I know, that although Charlotte could skip, play a tune with two fingers on a piano forte, and draw a *tumble-down* house with a pen or pencil, she could not read three lines without spelling, and never had a dozen words to spell but that she made ten mistakes in repeating them.

Emily's great delight was in her books, and what was strange in such a child, she liked nothing so well to read of as the old Kings and Queens. She had a small History of England which was always in her hand, and she could repeat all the principal things which had happened in the reigns of the Edwards, the Richards, and the Henrys, but her favourite was Elizabeth, and having seen a painting of that Queen at a noble-man's house which her Mamma had taken her to see, she went home so full of it, that she could not rest till she had got her maid to assist her to dress her doll in the fashion of Queen Elizabeth, and when she had done it, she surprised all the family by taking her down to the garden where they were walking, and leading her towards them, said, " my doll's like old Queen Bess."

POLITENESS.

THERE was once a young lady who was very plain in her person, but was so foolish and so vain, that she fancied herself quite beautiful, and that her shape was admired by every one who looked at her; but she was very much mistaken, for as she had never been obedient when she was a little girl, the more she was desired to hold up herself, the more she stooped and squeezed herself into a corner, so that she was more awkward than I can possibly tell you; and when-ever she moved to walk across the room, she twisted herself into so many odd shapes, that she was quite ridiculous.

So far this young lady is the only one to be blamed, and I wish I had nothing more to relate, but I cannot help it. I do not only wish my little readers, when they see any thing wrong in others, not to imitate the fault, but that they should never laugh at, or make a mock of it; and if little George and his sister Fanny had followed my advice, they would not be at this moment confined to the nursery, after having been sent, in disgrace, out of the drawing-room.

The young lady above-mentioned went a few days since to visit their Mamma, and as soon as she entered the room, a gentleman nearly as

fantastical as herself rose up to give her a chair. The rest of the company, whatever they thought, were too well bred to laugh, or appear to take notice of the bowing and twisting of the gentle-man and lady; but George and Fanny, I am sorry to say it, stood up directly behind them, he imitating one and Fanny the other, in such a manner that they thought every one present would be much amused with their cleverness; but they were disappointed, they frowned instead of laughing, and their Mamma ordered them both to quit the drawing-room, and forbid them to enter it again till they knew better how to behave themselves.

NOISY CECILIA.

So now, my little readers, as I am almost tired, I will finish my long account of good children and naughty ones, by saying a word or two of the most noisy little creature I ever met with in my life; and as she was a younger sister, and had several brothers and sisters who were very good children, you will not think I am partial to *all* the young ones, though I have mentioned two or three who have behaved better than their elders.

As to Miss Cecilia R. I assure you I could not have lived in the house with her on any account. At six o'clock in the morning the noise began; if her maid would not let her out of the nursery, she would take up any thing she could get at, and drum upon the table till she awoke every creature in the house; and when she got down into the hall, her delight was to make the great dog bark, or bring in her little cart full of stones, and if she could run with it till it overset, and the stones rolled about till the servants came to

see what was the matter, she was the more delighted.

At dinners she made so much noise by rattling her fork and spoon on her plate, that the servants could not hear when they were asked for any thing, so she was sent to dine in the nursery, and she was so troublesome every where, that nobody could bear her company.

No one however was so much disturbed by her as her poor Grandmamma, who would have loved her very much indeed, if she had been a good child; but she could not bear to see her come into her room, because she knew she would give her the head-ache and make her ill all day; and she never minded what was said to her, but grew worse and worse; and went one morning into her Grandmamma's room when she was reading, beating the drum with one hand and holding a trumpet to her mouth with the other, and the poor old lady was almost distracted; so Miss Cecilia was sent to a great distance to school, and not allowed to come home till she left off her naughty noisy tricks.

Blind Man

The Good Grandson

Turn - About - Johnny

The Naughty Girl

Nine Pins

90

The Parental Instructor

CHARLES and Mary were the children of Mr Elliot, a gentleman of fortune and elegant manners, who, having received a liberal education himself, was anxious, by his own instructions, to form the minds of his children to virtue; and he was perfectly adequate to the task. He was remarkably fond of his family, and they returned his affection with respect and love. Fond of their studies, these children never thought of amusement until they had learned the lessons pointed out by their father; and they always sat in the library till this was accomplished. Charles, who was older than Mary, having one day finished his task sooner than usual, earnestly entreated his father to tell a fine story, and called on his sister Mary to come and hear it. " Come, papa," said the little Charles, " you must favour us either with the tale of Cinderella, Ass-skin, Tom Thumb, or Bluebeard."

" What ! " said Mr Elliot, " at your age— would you wish me to relate stories which have not even the shadow of common sense in them ? It would really be ridiculous, to see a great big boy of ten years of age, and a young lady of nine, listening, with open mouths, to the adventures of an OGRE who ate little children, or the Little Gentleman with his Seven-league Boots; I could only pardon it in a child, who requires to be rocked asleep by his nurse."

" But papa," said Charles, " these stories are very amusing." " Yes, my dear, but what benefit can you derive from them ? Absurdities like these only serve to vitiate your taste and weaken your mind, while some of them excite terror and disgust." " Oh, papa, I know very well that there are neither ogres nor fairies." " When that is the case," returned his father,

" why are you so anxious to hear about these chimeras ? What benefit can you derive from the story of the Beautiful Princess who slept an hundred years ? I fear that, by accustoming yourself to learn such stories, you will be disgusted with what is useful and of real importance, and relinquish beneficial conversations and instructive reading, to run after frivolous books, or listen to childish tales." " Papa," replied Charles, " you know better what is suitable for us than we do ourselves; but may I venture to inquire why you make us learn the Fables of La Fontaine by heart, in which there are ravens and foxes that speak ? These animals are quite as extraordinary as fairies and ogres; for instance, the stork who gives the alarm of famine at the hillock of the ants, her neighbours, exists no more than the wolf which converses with Little Red-Riding-Hood ! "

" Charles," returned Mr Elliot, " you are now reasoning like a man; therefore let us discourse together a little. What you have said is very true, for the speaking stork does not exist any more than the blue bird and the cat in boots; but the story of the bird does not contain any moral; that is, there is nothing results from the reading of it that can afford you instruction, while the stork gives a very important lesson, by making us sensible of the necessity of preparing, during our youth, resources which may be of the most essential service in old age,—and here lies the difference between the fables of La Fontaine and the fairy tales." " Oh, papa," replied Charles, " I have always thought that we must give up those fine stories, where we meet with so many diamond castles, and magic wands which perform

91

such prodigies." " I would advise you to do so," returned his father; " although by this I do not mean to forbid you all entertaining reading; for there are many books by which you may be amused and instructed at the same time. I have arranged for your use, my children, a collection of Anecdotes and Stories, with which I intend both to amuse and instruct you, in place of your fairy tales; and whenever you please me I shall relate one of them, accompanied with such suitable reflections as, I am certain, will furnish sufficient matter for interesting conversation. I can assure you, that there are some of these anecdotes even more interesting than the best of your fairy tales; and what ought to render them still more agreeable to you is, that all the stories which I mean to relate to you have an excellent moral, and many of the persons mentioned are real characters. Besides, these persons are not Alexanders and Cæsars, princes, nor even grown up men, but only children! yes, children like yourselves, and who would have taken part in all your amusements if an opportunity had presented itself. These are heroes who will not dazzle you, and concerning whom you are at full liberty to form an opinion. What they have done you may likewise do. Besides, it is as much for your instruction as for your amusement that I wish to relate to you their actions; they are models which I propose for you. If they have shewn a good example, it is your duty to imitate them. If they have made rapid progress in their studies, what should prevent you from doing the same? If I represent to you a boy who has shewn the most lively fraternal love, it is to shew you an example of virtue,

which ought always to have a place in your hearts. In relating to you the actions of a good son or daughter, who have suffered for their parents, I please myself with the reflection, that I speak to children who are ready to imitate their example. In one word, I will only entertain you with models suitable to your age, in order to prevent you from telling me they are beyond your imitation.

" Now, my children, we shall begin this very day, because I am well satisfied with your conduct. The first I mean to relate to you is the story of a boy, whose courage is worthy of imitation."

FILIAL AFFECTION.

VOLNEY BECKNER, who was born at Londonderry in Ireland, felt an early desire for the sea—perhaps from his father being by profession a sailor. One day, being then only between seven and eight years of age, he persuaded his sister, who was rather older than himself, to go into a leaky boat, which lay fastened to the beach, when the sea was very rough; and having loosened it, for the purpose of going out to sea, they would undoubtedly have both been drowned, if a fisherman had not run to the place, and, after wading in, got hold of the rope, and dragged the boat ashore.

He had only reached his twelfth year, when he served with his father in an English vessel. His father, who knew by experience the dangers which a mariner runs, had taught him to swim; so that he cut the waves, plunged, and swam on the surface of the water with nearly as much facility and lightness as a fish! His greatest amusement, when his other occupations would permit him, was to swim round the vessel, and when he was weary, he would seize a cord, and in an instant leap on board the ship.

One day the child of a passenger, a very little girl, by means of the rolling of the ship, fell into the sea. The father of Volney, who happened to be present, sprang in after her, and soon caught her by the clothes; but as this brave mariner was regaining the vessel, and holding the child close to his bosom, he perceived a terrible shark pursuing him.—The shark is a large and strong fish, with an enormous mouth, armed with teeth, which cut and break the hardest bone.—The whole crew ran to the part where Beckner was trembling for his life, and fired their carbines at the monster, yet none durst go to his assistance.—The shark, who was not wounded, had already opened his horrid mouth, and was about to seize his prey, when a hideous shriek was given by all on board.

At the same moment, some one was observed to leap into the water. It was young Volney, armed with a large pointed sabre. He immediately plunged in, and went straight to the shark, which, stopping for a moment, gave him time to slide under his belly, into which he struck the sabre to the very hilt, and the desire of saving his father gave additional force to his arm. Against him the shark now turned his rage; but Volney avoided him, and gave him several fresh stabs.—During this combat they had thrown from the ship's side several ropes, and the father and the son each seized one.—They were drawn out of the sea, and every one began to rejoice.—Their comrades thought them safe; but, horrid to relate ! at that moment the monster, furious with his wounds, and still more furious at losing his prey, made a last and powerful effort. He plunged deep in the water, in order to take a more vigorous spring, and then, throwing himself above the waves, raised his horrid open mouth, and swallowed half the body of the young Volney, separating it from the other half, which remained suspended by the cord. This direful spectacle petrified all the spectators, and old Beckner, arrived on board, was in the utmost despair at having survived his son; but the son cast his last look upon the author of his life and seemed, even while dying, to feel pleasure in having preserved his father from the fatal accident of which he himself became the victim.

The Dangers of Swimming

To bathe in warm wea-ther, in lakes or ri-vers, is said to be ve-ry heal-thy. Lit-tle boys should be care-ful not to go out of their depth; for want of this care ma-ny have lost their lives: not by sharks or whales, but by not be-ing a-ble to swim when in deep wa-ter. Yet those who can swim are not al-ways safe; the cramp may take a good swim-mer, and if no help be at hand, he may lose his life. Lit-tle boys should not bathe with-out a pro-per per-son be-ing with them.

On the coast of A-fri-ca, and in the West In-dies, the cli-mate be-ing ve-ry warm, bath-ing is a great re-fresh-ment; but, one day as a lad was bath-ing in the har-bour of the Ha-van-nah, he was sei-zed by a shark, which had got one of his legs in its mouth, and be-fore as-sist-ance could be gi-ven him, he lost his leg; and his friends thought it a mer-cy he did not lose his life.

The Alphabet of Goody Two Shoes

A, was an Apple,
   And put in a pie,
With ten or twelve others,
   All piled up so high.

B, was tall Biddy,
   Who made the puff paste,
And put sugar and lemon-peel
   Quite to my taste.

C, is a Cheese,
   But don't ask for a slice,
For it serves to maintain
   A whole nation of Mice.

D, was Dick Dump,
   Who did nothing but eat,
And would leave book and play,
   For a nice bit of meat.

E, is an Egg,
   In a basket with more,
Which Jimmy will sell
   For a shilling a score.

F, was a Forester,
   Dressed all in green,
With a Cap of fine fur,
   Like a King or a Queen.

G, was a Greyhound,
   As swift as the wind ;
In the race of the course
   Left all others behind.

H, was a Hoyden ;
   Not like you, nor like me ;
For she tumbled about
   Like the waves of the sea.

I, was the ice
   On which William would skate ;
So up went his heels,
   And down went his pate.

J, was Joe Jenkins,
   Who play'd on the fiddle,
And began twenty tunes,
   But left off in the middle.

K, was a Kitten,
   Who jump'd at a cork,
And learn't to eat mice
   Without plate, knife, or fork.

And L, was a Lady,
   Who made him so wise ;
But he tore her long train,
   And she cried out her eyes.

M, was Miss Mira,
 Who turn'd in her toes,
And poked down her head,
 Till her knees met her nose.

And N, Mr. Nobody,
 Just come from France ;
Said he'd set her upright,
 And teach her to dance.

O, a grave owl :
 To look like him, Tom tried ;
So he put on a mask,
 And sat down by his side.

P, was a pilgrim,
 With a staff in his hand,
Return'd weary and faint
 From a far distant land.

Q, was the Queen
 Of Spades, I've heard say,
In her black velvet girdle,
 Just dress'd for the play.

Here's Ralph with the Raree-show,
 Calling so loud ;
But I'd rather give two-pence
 To look at the crowd.

And U, an Umbrella
 Saved Bell t'other day
From a shower that fell,
 Whilst she turn'd the new hay.

V, was a Village,
 Where lived near the brook
The renown'd Goody Two Shoes,
 Who sends you this Book.

W, was a Witch,
 Who set off at noon
To visit her cousin,
 The Man in the Moon.

X, was Xantippe,
 As you've heard before ;
But, not to forget her,
 I name her once more.

Y, was a youth,
 Who walked in the Park,
And play'd on the Flute,
 Till he made the Dogs bark.

Z, was a Zealander,
 Whose name was Van Bley ;
So here ends my song,
 And I wish you Good-day.

SAILING BOATS.

Take care little George and do not fall into the water. He appears very much pleased with his boat, and well he may be, as it was given him for being a good boy and learning his lesson.

His brother who had a present from his uncle, wishes to launch his vessel also, but he is very patient, waiting till his brother shall get out of his way.

How pleasant it is to see brothers and sisters agree and love one another, and always give way to each other rather than contend and be fretful.

When to the pond you take a trip,
To sail your pretty little ship,
Mind in the water not to slip.

STEAM PACKET.

These vessels pass through the water with great velocity, are fitted up in a magnificent style, and carry letters and passengers, from one place across the water to another.

Of the steam engine and other astonishing inventions, you may read when you are capable of understanding them.

See yonder Boat propelled by steam,
Is moving o'er the liquid stream,
As swiftly as a passing dream.
With fire and water well supplied,
Her engine good, and skill to guide
She cares not for the wind or tide.

SLIDING ON ICE.

Well this indeed looks like winter; take care little boy and do not go on the ice before some person older and wiser than yourself gives you permission, many serious accidents have happened from its breaking with persons on it, and most of them from carelessness or imprudence.

If you would learn to skate you should go to Holland, as the Dutch go many miles on the ice, and carry their provisions with them to the markets on their heads. How wonderful must that great God be, who can thus turn the water as it were into a stone.

Before you venture on the ice,
Take care it be not thin,
Lest underneath your feet it break,
And quickly throw you in.

TRUNDLING THE HOOP.

This is indeed a very good sport for little boys, but only in cool weather; some little boys make themselves very hot, and then drink cold water or sit down on the damp ground, by which means they often become very ill.

Idle Hours Employed

EVENING V.

THE weather having proved extremely wet, Mrs. Woodbine was prevented from taking her usual walk, and the children could not even amuse themselves in the garden. They were therefore extremely glad when the hour arrived for resuming their entertaining stories, and when Maria, placing herself by the side of her mamma, read the tale called

LITTLE ZOE.

LITTLE ZOE was such a kind and sweet tempered child, that when she was but three years old, all her young friends were delighted to have her in their company; and if her head happened to ache, or she were otherwise unwell, she was sure to be tenderly nursed by the eldest of the party, whilst the others brought out all their playthings in order to excite her attention, and, if possible, to divert her mind.

When she had attained the age of six years, she was one day left in the house alone; her father and mother having gone on a visit to one of their friends, her brothers being at school, and the servants having gone out upon various errands.

Zoe said to herself, " I am now mistress of my actions; and, as nobody sees me, I can do whatever I will; yet, though I am completely alone, if I do any thing wrong, I may injure myself. I will behave, therefore, as if my papa and mamma were at my side."

She then began to write a page, according to her master's desire; and afterward, going to the piano-forte, she played the last lesson which she had learned. After this, she sat down during half an hour to work; and at last she went into the garden to water the flowers, prop them up, and transplant some that belonged to her brothers, from one bed to another.

The evening came, and Zoe was well satisfied with herself, and with her day's employment. When her papa and mamma came home, she ran to meet them. Her mamma looked at her, and perceiving that she had an air of satisfaction; " I see clearly, my dear," said she, " that you have been very good to-day; if you had not been so, you would not be so well pleased with yourself. Be always good, and you will always be happy."

Zoe promised that she would, and made a resolution to keep her word. Her mamma having afterwards asked what she had done, she related to her the employments of the day: she showed what she had written; mentioned the lesson she had played, and let her mamma see how much she had worked. This gave her mamma so much pleasure that she embraced Zoe tenderly, and told her she had been a very good and obedient child.

The next day, Zoe's brothers went into the garden, and, having looked over their flowers, they saw some in new places. They doubted not that it was their good sister who planted them. They went immediately, therefore, to thank her. " Dear Zoe," said they, " you have given us some very pretty flowers;—tell us whether we can do any thing to please you in return ? " But Zoe was too good to ask for any thing.

Her brothers returned into the garden, picked out the finest flowers from their beds, and transplanted them into those of their dear sister; and to show still more how much they were delighted by her kindness, they went every morning into their gardens to gather a nosegay for her acceptance.

At the end of a few weeks, Zoe's mother received a visit from one of her neighbours. Zoe had scarcely entered the room when the lady exclaimed, " This is the dear little girl who is so good when her father and mother are from home ! I had a great deal of pleasure the other day," added she, " in seeing from my window how this amiable child behaved in the parlour and in the garden, though no person was with her. She did every thing with the same order and application as if her father and mother had been present."

Zoe blushed at this unexpected praise; she retired immediately from the company; and being alone in her chamber, she said, while the tears started into her eyes: " Oh ! how much is gained by being good, even when we believe ourselves to be alone ! Nothing that we do remains concealed. Mamma, at first sight, knew that I had been good, though I had not told her so; and even this lady saw what I did, though I did not think that any person witnessed my actions. If, then, I had done any thing wrong, it would have been the same. Ah ! what shame I should have suffered if this lady had seen me do any evil ! How she would have despised me ! And how much sorrow that I would have given to my dear papa and mamma ! I will always behave well, even when I find myself in the greatest

solitude; recollecting that, wherever I am, the eye of my Creator is upon me; and to Him I must look for that blessing which is the reward of a virtuous life."

EVENING VI.

One fine evening Emma was appointed to read to our little party; and on opening the book she said with a smile, " I have myself been giving *advice*, this afternoon, to our neighbour William Lockett; who, having lost a beautiful robin, which he had lately caught, was very gravely walking through our field, holding the empty cage in his hand, with the door open, in order to lure the little wanderer back again. I told him, however, that it was quite in vain for him to expect that a bird which had the use of its wings, would return to the prison whence he had so happily escaped; and I advised him never again to confine one of those pretty creatures, which delight us with their innocent warblings when they are at liberty, but are almost sure to die in a short time when they are shut up in a cage, and deprived of their natural food."

" I wish he may attend to your admonition," said Mrs. Woodbine.

EVENING VIII.

THE SPOILED CHILDREN.

Mr. Beaufoy had two sons whom he tenderly loved, but did not spoil. He gave them an excellent education, and inured them to such habits as promised to render their constitutions healthy and vigorous. Though he possessed a handsome fortune, he seldom permitted them to partake of rich meats or to drink wine; he also accustomed them to early rising, to washing themselves with cold water, to sleeping in a cold bed in the winter, and to taking daily exercise without fearing a little wind or rain.

Mr. Robinson's children were very differently managed; they had coffee, chocolate, wine, tarts, and all sorts of sweetmeats, as often as they thought proper; water was warmed in the morning to wash them; their beds were warmed in the evening; and they were not permitted to go out if the weather were cold or cloudy.

One day, Philip and James were talking with their father; and, without presuming to complain of the manner in which they were educated, they happened to say, according to what they had heard, that the little Robinsons were very happy.

Mr. Beaufoy, to undeceive them, proposed to them to go with him to pay a visit to Mr. Robinson, whose home was at the distance of some miles from his own. This proposition was received with joy; and the next morning, they set out in a post-chaise.

The journey was a very cheerful one; but when they arrived, what a sight presented itself to their eyes!

On entering the apartment, they saw three children in the most miserable condition: their faces yellow, their eyes dull and hollow, their teeth black and broken; and they were altogether so weak and so meagre, that people might have supposed they did not get enough to eat.

Mrs. Robinson complained with tears in her eyes, that for eight days past, her fourth son had been obliged to keep his bed; and, soon after, she brought a large glass of medicine, and made each of the children drink his share.

At table, Mr. Robinson's children appeared to be disgusted with every thing, and to care for nothing. On the other hand, their guests, Philip and James, ate cheerfully of whatever was set before them. There was even a plate of cucumbers, a vegetable rather indigestible, of which they ate heartily.

Mrs. Robinson asked them, with an air of concern, if so doing would not make them ill? and she added, that she should think her children would be killed if she permitted them to taste such food.

She was perfectly astonished when they replied, that they were used to such things, and that nothing made them ill.

Some time after they had dined, Mr. Beaufoy took leave of Mr. and Mrs. Robinson; and on returning home, he sent his children to their cold bed at an early hour as usual.

The next day, they came skipping to wish their papa good morning: their little cheeks were as red as roses, and an air of health gave lustre to their whole countenance.

"How happy I am," said their papa, "to have children so gay, and so healthy! I should be truly afflicted if I saw you languid and weak like the Robinsons. What do you think of those children?"

"O dear, papa," replied Philip, "those poor

children excite our pity: they look like shadows; and appear as if they were going to die. We would not be in their place for all the gold in the world."

"But," replied their father, "if I were to rear you as tenderly as they are reared; if I had your bed warmed, and the water, in which you are to wash, heated; if I were to give you wine and chocolate; if, instead of the simple meats which we have at dinner, I should teach you to relish some dainty, would you not be better pleased?"

"No, no, papa!" cried they, "we prefer cold beds and cold water, and nothing but plain food, to being made sick with rich meats and warm beds."

"I am delighted, my dear boys," said the father, "that you know how to prize the health you enjoy. I hope that you will never again envy the lot of the little Robinsons, and that you will understand that your father, in educating you with less delicacy, only seeks your happiness."

The lesson which Mr. Beaufoy gave to James and Philip was but too forcibly illustrated by what happened afterward to Mr. Robinson's children. The boy that was ill when Mr. Beaufoy visited that gentleman, died in the course of a few days. Two other sons, also, died in the following year, and in this manner:—Seeing, one day in the winter, some children at play upon the ice, they had a great desire to take part in the amusement: they went, therefore, to their mother, and persuaded her to walk for half an hour with them. On returning to the house, however, it appeared that they had taken a violent cold; and though their mother put them to bed, and made them take various medicines, they died in a few days.

101

Only the eldest son now remained; and though he did not die so early as the others, he was the subject of illness all his life.

At the age of twenty-four, he was as weak as an old man, and was obliged to have a fire in his chamber every day; for even in summer, he complained that he was never warm. His stomach was so weak that it could bear nothing but boiled veal, lamb, or chickens; and he one day expected to die because he had eaten a small slice of bacon. So true it is, that those who wish to enjoy good health, should be accustomed to a hardy mode of life.

The History of Sweetpea

TO describe, gentle reader, the little Person with whom I am about to make you acquainted, I must draw his picture.—My little fat friend, then, I shall introduce by the name of SWEETPEA,— being so pleasant a lad, that no flower in the garden could better suit the comparison—His looks were mild and gentle—He was one of those happy children on whose countenance good-nature had placed two sweet dimples.—He was mighty active at tumbling, notwithstanding his make was rather against such exploits, being the very greatest likeness possible to those little *fat white gentry* we frequently see tumble out of a nut.—Our little man had some very good friends in town, and every Christmas a large parcel of plums were sent the little SMILERS, who used to jump round a large dish of *snap-dragon*, over which they burnt their *fingers*, and sometimes their *mouths*. It was on one fine pleasant evening, in the height of Summer, that our SWEETPEA had been running and tumbling with his little companions, when, tired with play, he laid himself down upon the grass, and fell asleep. When he awoke he looked round with surprise, and seeing his brothers coming to find him, he started up.—I have such a pleasant story to tell you, my boys, says he;—come with me, and I will get *you*, FREDERICK, to write it out—for though it is but a dream, it is a very clever one, I promise you.— They then placed themselves at their table, the little Commodore dipped his pen in the ink and thus began:

The Dream.

After I had laid myself down I fell asleep, and I thought I heard a sound like a trumpet—I then

saw a large party of horse-men cloathed in scarlet. After them came a nice Tim-whisky, with six beautiful white hobbies; on the sides of the carriage were painted Sweetpeas, Roses, and Sweet-briar. Upon their arrival, they presented a wreath of flowers, with which they crowned me, and placed me in the whisky—Immediately a shout proclaimed me *King* of the good boys—We flew through the air, and I found myself at the King's palace. He smiled upon me, and turning to his little son, " Observe," says he, " that dutiful child, he fears God—he honours his parents."—I was struck with astonishment, and bowing with the most profound respect, I some how turned myself upon my Dog *Trusty's* tail, (who laid close behind me) his barking awoke me, which finished my dream.

The boys ran down stairs with the paper to their Father, who commended the writing:—It was indeed an agreeable dream, says he, and I will add a few words at the bottom of your paper.—

" Who would not rejoice at the smiles of
" Majesty, and more so when crowned with so
" much goodness ?—Yet, my dear Sweetpea,
" were your sleeping thoughts realised, I should
" warn you to beware of pride; always keep in
" your mind, that no earthly Prince can be equal
" to the King of Kings. Nor can the favours of
" the rich (if wicked men) be an object worthy
" your imitation. Turn then thine eyes, thou
" dear child, from wicked men and boys; regard
" not their laughing at your just actions,—but in
" some retired corner kneel down, bend your
" head and heart before your God, he will place
" you, not to be the supporter of a Prince's train,
" but will adorn you with a crown of shining
" Gold, intermixed with flowers of Laurel that
" will never fade."

Scripture Histories

The Creation of the World.

IN six days God created the whole world out of nothing; that is to say, the heavens, the earth, fire, air, water, birds, beasts, fish, and every creeping thing. He made man also out of the dust of the earth, and called his name *Adam*. And unto *Adam* he gave power over the fish of the sea, the fowls of the air, the cattle, and every

thing that moved upon the face of the earth. And *Adam* was planted in the garden of *Eden* to dress it, and keep it, and was perfectly happy there: for he knew no sin.

Adam and Eve.

ADAM had not been long in the garden of *Eden*, before God Almighty thought fit to increase his happiness; and considering he was alone, threw him into a deep sleep, and took out one of his ribs, from which he formed *Eve*, a more beautiful creature than himself, and allotted her to be a help-meet for him. *Adam*, at first sight of this new and lovely companion, cried out with extacy of joy, *Bone art thou of my bone, and flesh of my flesh*. In this state of bliss, they lived but a short time; for *Satan*, envying their happiness, tempted the woman to eat of the fruit of the tree of knowledge, which God, to make trial of their obedience, had strictly charged them not to touch. The artful insinuations of the *serpent*, together with the beauty of the fruit, prevailed on her to transgress the divine law. She tasted, and was highly delighted, and by her winning behaviour, tempted her

husband to eat also. No sooner had they swallowed down the gilded bait, but their eyes were opened, they saw they were naked, and, conscious of their guilt, endeavoured to hide themselves in the garden from the wrath of their offended Creator; but he soon drove them from their secret recess; turned them out of their seat of bliss, and denounced thereupon not only a heavy curse upon the *serpent*, but on them likewise, though with this ray of mercy in his anger, *that the seed of the woman should bruise the* serpent's *head.*

Noah's Ark.

OF all *Adam's* sons, *Seth* was the best. He and his sons called on the name of the Lord; but in process of time, man indulging himself in all manner of riot and excess, God repented that he had made him; and determined to destroy the whole world by an universal flood. *Noah* however, who was one of *Seth's* posterity, found

grace in the eyes of the Lord. Whereupon God commanded him to build an ark of sufficient bulk for the reception of himself, his family, and two of each species of animals. No sooner were they entered than the windows of the heavens were opened, and it rained heavily for forty days and forty nights. By this general deluge every living substance was destroyed, except *Noah*, his wife, his three sons and their wives, and the other creatures that were admitted with them into the ark. But soon after the deluge ceased, the earth was stocked with inhabitants by the three sons of *Noah*, viz. *Shem, Ham, and Japheth.*

The Tower of Babel.

SOON after the sons of *Noah* had replenished the earth with inhabitants, they assembled

together in the fruitful plains of *Shinar*, where they erected the lofty Tower of *Babel*, and vainly attempted to raise its walls to the very skies, in hopes to make their names immortal; but God Almighty soon baffled their impious and ill-concerted project, confused their language so that they could not understand each other, and scattered and dispersed them in various tribes all round the world.

Solomon's Temple.

GOD Almighty having blessed *Solomon* the son of *David* (the wisest of all men) with peace and plenty, he determined to build a magnificent temple to the Lord on Mount *Moriah*. For which purpose he sent to *Hiram*, king of *Tyre*, his father's ancient friend, for cedar wood, and other materials requisite for the accomplishment of his pious design. All things being duly prepared, he erected a stately fabric three stories high, and embellished it within and without with a vast variety of fine carved works, profusely overlaid with gold. As soon as the whole was complete, *Solomon* summoned a numerous assembly of *Israelites*, and with the utmost pomp and splendour, dedicated this glorious building, by prayer and supplication, to the only true God.

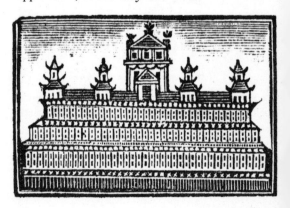

AN ELEGY

ON THE

Death and Burial

OF

OCK ROBIN.

Ornamented with Cuts.

YORK:

Printed by J. Kendrew, 23, Colliergate.

WHO kill'd Cock Robin?
I, says the Sparrow,
With my bow and arrow,
And I kill'd Cock Robin.

This is the Sparrow,
With his bow and arrow.

Who saw him die?
I, said the Fly,
With my little eye,
And I saw him die.

This is the Fly,
With his little eye.

Who caught his blood?
I, said the Fish,
With my little dish,
And I caught his blood.

This is the Fish,
That held the dish.

Who made his shroud?
I, said the Beetle,
With my little needle
And I made his shroud.

This is the Beetle,
With his thread and needle.

Who shall dig the grave?
I, said the Owl,
With my spade and shov'l,
And I'll dig his grave.

This is the Owl so brave,
That dug Cock Robin's grave.

Who will be the Parson?
I, said the Rook,
With my little book,
And I will be the Parson.

Here's parson Rook,
A reading his book.

Who will be the clerk?
I, said the Lark,
If 'tis not in the dark,
And I will be the clerk.

Behold how the Lark,
Says Amen, like a clerk.

Who'll carry him to the grave?
I, said the Kite,
If 'tis not in the night,
And I'll carry him to the grave.

Behold now the Kite,
How he takes his flight.

Who will carry the link,
I, said the Linnet,
I'll fetch it in a minute,
And I'll carry the link.

Who'll be the chief mourner?
I, said the Dove,
For I mourn for my love,
And I'll be the chief mourner.

Who'll bear the pall?
We, says the Wrens,
Both the cock and the hen,
And we,ll bear the pall.

Here's the Linnet with a light
Altho' 'tis not night.

Here's a pretty Dove,
That mourns for her love.

See the Wrens so small,
Who bore Cock Robin's pall.

Who'll sing a psalm?
I, says the Thrush,
As he sat in a bush,
And I'll sing a psalm.

Who'll toll the bell?
I, says the Bull,
Because I can pull,
So Cock Robin farewell.

Here's a fine Thrush,
Singing psalms in a bush.

All the birds in the air,
Fell a sighing and sobbing,
When they heard the bell toll
For poor Cock Robin.

Here we go up, up, up,
Here we go down, down, down;
Here we go backward and forward,
And here we go round, round, round.

Here's the tailor with his sheers,
To cut off bad children's ears.

Now to be good if you'll begin,
You shall have this fine house for to
live in.

And who could e'er desire more,
Here is the key to lock the door.

THE
HISTORY
OF
TTLE TOM TUCKER.

This is little Tom Tucker,
That sung for his Supper.

YORK:

J. Kendrew, Printer, Colliergate.

Little Tom Tucker,
  Sing for your supper,
What shall I sing for ?
  White bread and butter.
How shall I cut it,
  Without a knife ;
And how shall I marry
  Without ever a wife ?

Tho' little Tom Tucker,
Loved white bread and butter,
  He did not love learning his book ;
So when he went to school,
They drest him like a fool,
With a cap on his head, only look.

—

loved playing at top,
  often would stop
or to have a game in the street ,
  he knew 'twas a fault,
  if he was caught.
well might expect to be beat.

——

He loved for to play
By night or by day,
  He could trundle the hoop very
    well,
But though he knew better,
Than to learn one letter,
For fear they should learn him to spell

—

A man from the fair,
Came by with a bear,
  With a monkey that rode upon
    bruin ;
Tom followed to see,
More blocked was he.
  For it caus'd him to play the truant.
At home he got blame,
When next morning came,
  To school he went creeping quite
    sad.

re his master did flog,
  chain him to a log.
r being so naughty a lad,
  Tom, this won't do,
a dunce it is true,
l boys that can read are my
  betters ;
e learnt A, B, C,
D, E, F, G,
nd soon all the rest of his letters.

—

Then Tom learned to spell,
And went to school well,
  With satchel and books at his back ;
No more would he stay
To play by the way,
  With Ned, Bill, Harry, or Jack.

Then Tom learnt to read,
Quite pretty indeed,
  And very soon after to write ;
Now Tom was so good,
He might play when he would,
  Without being put in a fright.

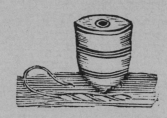

Tom kept learning his book,
And cheerful did look,
    Of the fool's cap no longer in fear;
Got his master's good word,
Was head scholar preferr'd,
    And the above fine medal to wear.

He had a whip and a top,
Bought for him at the shop,
    And a great many playthings beside,
And his father with joy,
Bid him keep a good boy,
    And he should have a horse for to
        ride.

This horse he soon got,
That could amble and trot,
    Only see how he gallops along;
He always at ease is,
And does as he pleases,
    But takes care he never does wro

One day he was out
And walking about,
    He met an old woman quite poor,
He gave her all his pence,
She returned him her thanks,
    And hoped he soon would have
        more.

One sun shining day,
He met a lady gay,
    And he being grown a smart youth,
He asked her to marry,
Not long did she tarry,
    For Tom promis'd he'd love her
        with truth.

Now Tom's got a wife,
And Tom's got a knife,
    And Tom can sit down to his sup
As blest as a king,
And each night can sing,
    After eating his white bread
        butter.

Jolly Welchman.

Little Husband.

The Brown Cow.

Taffy was a Welchman,
    And Taffy was a thief,
Taffy came to my house,
    And stole a piece of beef;
I went to Taffy's house,
    And Taffy was not at home,
Taffy came to my house,
    And stole a marrow-bone.

I had a little husband,
    No bigger than my thumb,
I put him in a pint pot,
    And there I bade him drum;
I gave him a pair of garters,
    To garter up his hose,
And a little handkerchief,
    To wipe his dirty nose.

I had a little brown cow,
    She gave a can of milk,
I sold my little brown cow,
    And bought a gown of si
There was three rows up,
    And three rows down,
Stand back you saucy Jack,
    You'll ruffle all my gown.

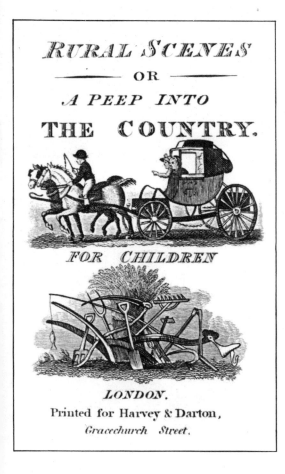

RURAL SCENES

OR

A PEEP INTO

THE COUNTRY.

FOR CHILDREN

LONDON.
Printed for Harvey & Darton,
Gracechurch Street.

INTRODUCTION

Come, little children, wake from sleep,
And into the country take a peep;
Already the sun is mounted high,
The lark sings merrily in the sky,
The air blows cheerly; roses gay
Bloom in the hedges, mix'd with May;
The drops of dew are lightly flung
From the green branches, where they hung;
The sheep-bell tinkles up the hill,
The water dances through the mill:
Come, little children, wake from sleep,
And into the country take a peep.

The lab'rer whistles o'er the mead,
The sower scatters wide his seed;
The cows wind lowing down the vale,
To Nancy, with her stool and pail;
And Giles the hen-house door unlocks,
To set at large the crowing cocks:
Come, little children, wake from sleep,
And into the country take a peep.

Down where the sparkling river shines,
The angler takes his rod and lines;
The sportsman ranges through the wood,
To find the purple pheasant's brood,
Or, wily, spreads the cruel snare,
To catch the gentle, timid hare:
Over the high-field's sloping brow,
Young Colin drives his even plough,
While, at his heel, the jetty crows
Pick up the insects as he goes.
Soon will the yellow harvest rise,
Warm'd by the heat of summer skies:
The brawny reapers, hot and brown,
Will cut the waving treasures down,
And shout the halloo largess song,
As the slow waggon creaks along.

Haste to the country, haste, before
The hollow wintry storm shall roar,
And the bleak wind, with bluster loud,
Drive sailing o'er the snowy cloud.
Come, little children, wake from sleep,
And into the country take a peep.

Feeding Poultry.

Come, here is a good breakfast for you; but
do not gobble so, my little duck ! I am really
ashamed to see you eat so greedily. Only look
at that pullet; she is just as hungry as you are,
and yet she takes only one little barley-corn at a
time: you cannot think how disagreeable it is
to see you eat such large mouthfuls.

The voice of the glutton I heard with disdain,
" I've not eaten this hour, I must eat again;
O ! give me a pudding, a pie, or a tart,
A duck, or a fowl, which I love from my heart:
How sweet is the picking
Of capon or chicken,
A turkey and chine,
Are most charming and fine;
To eat and to drink, all my pleasure is still,
I care not who wants, so that I have my fill."
O ! let me not be like the glutton inclined,
In feasting my body and starving my mind;
With moderate viands be thankful, and pray
That the Lord may supply me with food the
next day;
Not always a craving,
With hunger still raving;
But little and sweet
Be the food that I eat;

To learning and wisdom, O ! let me apply,
And leave to the glutton his pudding and pie.

Gathering Apples.

What fine fruit those nonsuch apples are ! either eaten ripe from the tree, or made into a dumpling or pudding, and boiled, or into a tart or pie, and baked. Take care, my lads, do not put too many into your pockets, as the farmer will let you eat plentifully, and, no doubt, pay you when the work is done.

Apples grow spontaneously in many woods of America, and are there so sweet as to need no sugar, either in pies or puddings.

Catching a Horse.

What, always at play, Smiler ! you have been galloping about this green meadow, or standing still under the great ash, without once thinking of work, for these three days ! Who, do you think, is to keep you for nothing, and find you a warm house in winter, and fine healthy pasture all summer long, merely that you may frolic, and sport, and be of no service in the world ? No, no ! he that will not work, neither shall he eat. A little play is well enough, but all play is a very bad maxim, as every school-boy could tell you.

Whether the horse, Smiler, understood all that was said to him, I cannot tell; but he seems to be going to the sieve for corn, and while he eats, the halter may be slipped over his ears, and he may be then led to the stable.

Nutting.

Though cherries and currants are stripp'd from
    the bough,
  And lilies, and roses, and violets fade,
The hedges are garnish'd with blackberries now,
  And nuts hang in clusters along the green shade.

Come, good girls and boys, to the grove and the
    wood,
  With basket and wallet, a nutting we'll go;
Not a naughty one here, I'll have none but the
    good,

110

Come, trip through the fields on a frolicsome
toe.
'Tis not, little bird, to dismantle thy nest;
'Tis not, gentle hare, to affright thee away;
'Tis not, pretty pheasant, to wound thy soft breast;
Nor, Robin, to stop thy sweet songs on the
spray.
Nor yet will we pluck the red berries that glow
On the hawthorn, to feed thee when winter
comes on;
It would not be honest to starve thee, and so
We'll take a few hedge-nuts, and quickly be
gone.

The Tinker.

There stands an old Tinker, he's mending a pan:
" You have got a black job there, I see, my good
man."
" Why, yes, Sir, 'tis dirty enough I agree;
But this is my maxim, and always shall be;
I'd rather have black hands, and plenty of meat,
Than ever such white ones, and nothing to eat."

The Traveller.

An intense frost has such an influence upon the
human body, when exposed to it, as to cause a
person to be almost irresistibly inclined to sleep;
and many have lost their lives from want of
resolution to resist the temptation. Even some
persons who have been well acquainted with the
danger, have been with great difficulty aroused; as
was the case with Dr. Solander and Sir Joseph
Banks, when accompanying Captain Cook on his
first voyage round the world.

" O come to my master," cries honest old Tray,
" The snow falls apace, and the night is so drear;
And the path is all hid, and he knows not his way:
Come, kind-hearted trav'ller, pray come to him
here."

Poor honest old Tray, with a pitiful cry,
Thus howl'd to the winds on the common so
wide;
But the night was so cold, not a creature came by,
And long before morning his master had died.

Oh! how did his wife turn her eyes to the door,
  And his children run out ev'ry minute to see:
But, alas! he shall never come back any more,
  Nor kiss them, nor dance them about on his
    knee:
Ah! no—here he lies on the common so bare,
And poor Tray is howling, to let them know
    where.

The Coach.

Ah! what comes here, rumbling so fast over the gravel and stones? The Colchester stage, heavily laden for London, just stopping at the sign of the Swan, for the horses and coachey to drink. Come, master coachman, make haste and finish that pot of porter, for your little inside passengers (who are going home to see their friends for the Christmas holidays) cannot imagine why you are stopping so long. Master Dicky would have put his head out of the window several times, to bid you cut up your horses a little more, if Patty, his little sister, had not pulled him back again by the sleeve: "For, Dicky," said she, "we would always be kind to the poor animals that drag us so willingly; and as for a few minutes, sooner or later, it is not worth while to make them suffer for it, poor things. Though I am sure I long to kiss dear papa and mamma, and brothers and sisters, as much as you do; and to give papa the nice shirt that I have been making for him, and the purse, and the watch-chain, and the——" "Huzza! there we are off again," said little Dick.

The Pedlar.

Now let me advise you, young woman, not to lay out your money for those scissors if you do not want them, though they be ever such a bargain. I am sure, that those your grandmother gave you for a fairing, will last you these many long years, with a penny or two for grinding; and if they are not quite so bright and stylish, what does that signify? for we should not judge by the look of a thing, but by the use of it.

The Chair-maker.

Well, Master Rush, is our chair done ? I am sure it wanted mending badly enough; for yesterday, when our Tray went to jump on it, intending, I suppose, to take a nap, plump ! he comes through on to the floor again. Ha ! ha ! ha ! I cannot help laughing, when I think of it. How he stared about, and looked so surprised, and so silly, through the bars of the chair. Poor Tray ! Pray, Master Rush, make haste and finish it. But I must not stand talking here, for I am going to fly my kite, in the meadow: there is a fine high wind, and you'll soon see it peeping over the tops of the houses.

The indigent Lad.

Poor perishing beggar ! my heart melts to see what a wretched case thou art in; with thread-bare jacket, full of great holes for the wind to whistle through, and without a morsel of shoe or stocking for thy poor thin legs, it is miserably hard to wander about in such a terrible evening, when the snow falls so fast, and the wind blusters so loud; and cold, dark night is coming on apace. Poor perishing beggar ! I am sorry to see the gentlefolks in that comfortable, warm parlour, sitting so carelessly, and never offering to give thee a morsel of victuals to eat, or a rag or two to throw over thy poor shivering back.

The Bats.

These bats have been hanging fast asleep by their hooked claws, all the dark and cold weather of winter; till this warm day made them begin to move, and open their eyes, and feel hungry, and they thought they would just peep abroad. But when they had stretched their stiff leathern wings, and were fluttering about, these two boys met them with their nets.

Fortune-telling.

Here are a wicked old woman, and two silly

young women. The old woman is wicked for pretending to know what she does not know; and the young women are silly for believing her. She is a gipsy, and calls herself a fortune-teller. Why, thirty years ago, this very old woman told simple Sally that she was to marry a handsome 'squire. So she turned off honest Tom the gardener; (for I fancy simple Sally did not know that honest gardeners are often better than handsome 'squires;) and she waited a great many years, expecting every day to see this fine person. But he never came; and now she is grown old, she sees the folly of having placed confidence in the silly predictions of a fortune-teller.

Angling.

My lad, you're so full of your fun and your slaughter,
  You'll fall, if you do not take care;
And I fancy, young fellow, you'd feel in the water,
  Much as fishes feel—when in the air.

The Robin and Child.

Come hither, sweet Robin, don't be so afraid,
  I would not hurt even a feather:
Come hither, sweet Robin, and pick up some bread,
  To feed you this very cold weather.

I don't mean to frighten you, dear little things,
  And pussy-cat is not behind me;
So hop about pretty, and drop down your wings,
  And pick up the crumbs, and don't mind me.

But ah ! the wind blows, and I must not stay long,
  I shall let all the snow and the sleet in;
So remember next summer to give me a song,
  And pay for the breakfast you're eating.

Fish Machine.

This man is driving to some great town to sell his fish to the inhabitants. He not only serves them, but also the fishermen and himself. Indeed, they find a mutual help in each other; for it would be very difficult always to find a

market on the sea-coast, and equally inconvenient to the townspeople to go there for them. If he carries fish only, he pays no turnpikes.

Mending the Road.

Observe how soon children may become useful. Here is a lad who can do almost as much as a man, and by his labour earns not only money enough to keep himself, but some towards keeping his little brothers and sisters. How pleasing will it be to him to reflect, when he is grown up, that, instead of having been a burden to his parents, he has been a help to them. Their poverty is a blessing to him, and not an evil: by it he has learnt to be industrious, and he has it in his power now, to repay them for the trouble he gave them when he was a helpless infant.

The Gipsies.

See, here are the Gipsy-folks, boiling their pot,
With the wood they have been to the hedges and
    got,

For they have no cottage to put themselves under,
Because they are idle, and so 'tis no wonder;
But always they wander about up and down,
With their hair hanging straight on their
    shoulders so brown,
And a few dirty rags hung in tatters about 'em,
For those who won't work for things, must go
    without 'em:
So they tell people's fortunes, and promise them
    too,
To be ladies, and lords, and I cannot tell who.
Fine people, to promise such wonderful matters,
Who can't keep themselves out of rags and of
    tatters!
No, no, if they had any wit, they'd have guess'd
That to work for one's living is always the best.

School.

Within the neat cottage, beside the tall tree,
Jemima is learning her A, B, C, D;
And I think I can guess, by her sensible look,
That she'll make a brave scholar at learning her
    book.

I'm sure that she does not look this way and that,
At the bird, or the bee, or the dog, or the cat;
Or crumple the leaves with her finger or thumb;
Or gape, and keep wishing that play-time would
    come:
No, no, she knows better than that, I can see,
And what a brave scholar she's likely to be !

The Fiddler.

Here is the poor blind fiddler, who goes from
place to place, playing nearly the same tunes
every where: he looks as if he wanted a meal of
good victuals; but his little boy seems to be
very healthy. The farmer appears to be feeling
in his pocket, for some halfpence to give the
poor musician, whose scraping may have pleased
his wife and child.

I wander up and down here, and go from street to
    street,
But 'tis hard to fiddle many tunes with nothing for
    to eat;
So, lady, put a halfpenny into my ragged hat,
For when I get a bit of bread, I'm very glad of
    that.

MISTRESS TOWL.

There was an Old Woman named Towl,
Who went out to Sea with her Owl,
But the Owl was Sea-sick,
And scream'd for Physic ;
Which sadly annoy'd Mistress Towl.

OLD WOMAN OF CROYDON.

There was an Old Woman of Croydon,
To look young she affected the Hoyden,
And would jump and would skip,
Till she put out her hip ;
Alas poor Old Woman of Croydon.

OLD WOMAN OF BATH.

There was an Old Woman of Bath,
And She was as thin as a Lath,
She was brown as a berry,
With a Nose like a Cherry ;
This skinny Old Woman of Bath.

OLD WOMAN OF EALING.

There was an Old Woman of Ealing,
She jump'd till her head touch'd the Ceiling
When 2 1 6 4,
Was announc'd at her Door ;
As a prize to th'Old Woman of Ealing.

OLD WOMAN OF LYNN.

OLD WOMAN OF EXETER.

There liv'd an Old Woman at Lynn,

Whose Nose very near touch'd her chin,

You may easy suppose,

She had plenty of Beaux;

This charming Old Woman of Lynn.

There dwelt an Old Woman at Exeter,

When visitors came it sore vexed her,

So for fear they should eat,

She lock'd up all the meat;

This stingy Old Woman of Exeter.

OLD WOMAN OF HARROW.

OLD WOMAN OF GOSPORT.

There was an Old Woman of Harrow,

Who visited in a Wheel barrow,

And her servant before,

Knock'd loud at each door;

To announce the Old Woman of Harrow.

There was an Old Woman of Gosport

And she was one of the cross sort,

When she dress'd for the Ball;

Her wig was too small;

Which enrag'd this Old Lady of Gospo

THE AFFECTIONATE
PARENT'S GIFT,
AND THE
Good Child's Reward;
CONSISTING OF
A SERIES OF POEMS AND ESSAYS,
ON
NATURAL, MORAL, AND RELIGIOUS SUBJECTS;
Calculated to lead the tender Minds of Youth in the early Practice of Virtue
and Piety, and thereby promote their temporal
Prosperity and eternal Happiness.

TO WHICH IS PREFIXED,

AN AFFECTIONATE ADDRESS
ON THE
Duties and Obligations they owe to God and their Parents.

———

By HENRY SHARPE HORSLEY.

———

ILLUSTRATED BY
UPWARDS OF ONE HUNDRED AND FOURTEEN ENGRAVINGS

———

VOL. I.

LONDON:
PRINTED FOR T. KELLY, 17, PATERNOSTER ROW,
By J. Rider, Little Britain.

1828.

PREFACE

It is an acknowledged fact, and much to be lamented, that the greater part of the Books published for the use of children, are either ridiculous in themselves, unfit to instruct or inform, or are of an improper tendency, calculated only to mislead the susceptible and tender minds of youth; and, consequently, ought to be rejected by parents and guardians of children with as much indignation, as a proffered poisonous ingredient for mixture or infusion into the food of their children.

Every intelligent parent will unquestionably acknowledge the existing difficulty in making a suitable selection of subjects, so as to attract the attention of Juvenile readers, and in clothing the sentiments intended to be conveyed to infant minds in language suitable to their capacities of comprehension. I am perfectly aware of these existing difficulties; and, in making this remark,

I profess not to possess any method more adroit for the accomplishment of so desirable an end superior to others, but in sincerity of intention, for the benefit of the rising generation, I yield to none.

Every one must acknowledge that a great deal depends upon the first impressions on the juvenile mind; and, at the same time, must admit that the mind of a child is extremely susceptible.

In a country professing Christianity, it is to be lamented that individuals are to be found, who will lend themselves to the preparation of mental food for children's minds of such objectionable and contaminating qualities, as is to be met with in the present day. It must be admitted, that the minds of children are equally athirst for novelty, in common with persons of maturer years; but that thirst after novelty ought to be kept within the restricted limits of prudence by those who have the control over them, and the culture of their minds entrusted to their care.

In the present little Work, I have endeavoured to select such subjects of a familiar kind, and have so accommodated them to the purpose intended, as I thought best calculated to awaken the energies of the mind; and, when once awakened, to lead them by easy and gentle steps to the contemplation of that Being, from whom flows every good that we enjoy. I have endeavoured to pourtray vice in its heinous character, and its evil tendencies;—to picture the milder virtues of the mind, as being alone worthy of cultivation. I have also endeavoured to enforce obedience, and inculcate sincerity and truth; I have directed the infant mind to the true and only source of genuine comfort,—*i.e.* a saving knowledge of our Lord and Saviour; I have invariably strove to create a love for the reading the Holy Scriptures: in connection with that view, I have grounded several of the Poems upon the most interesting historical relations, as being the best calculated to awaken a desire for Scriptural study and information; and, I trust, that the moral tendency of the whole will prove a sufficient passport into the hands of children generally.

I am sensible that I have not to boast of the silver-toned lyre of a Byron, a Scott, &c. &c.; but, if the humble offering of my muse is not drest in the language of eloquence, it is clad in the plain garb of honest sincerity; and if I succeed in drawing the minds of my Juvenile readers to the contemplation of that God, who is ever well pleased with sincerity of intention;— if I succeed in curbing the too prevalent practice of dealing in superlatives, which, if analyzed, cannot be considered, either more or less, than an indirect species of lying;—if I awaken a love and regard for truth, and create sentiments of gratitude, obedience, and humanity, in the bosoms of those into whose hands this humble effort may fall, I have gained my point—I have succeeded in my design.

HENRY SHARPE HORSLEY.

THE POOR CRIPPLE GIRL.

Two little sisters had got leave
    To walk into the fields,
With little baskets for to pluck
    Wild flowers—which nature yields.

Being very good, their mother gave
    A penny unto each;
To buy some gingerbread when'ere
    A standing they would reach.

They trudg'd along, when one espied
    A little cleanly girl,
Going hopping on a wooden crutch
    With gingerbread to sell.

I'll spend my penny, Sarah said,
    Perhaps her cakes are fine;
But Mary said, I'm sure she's poor,
    I'll freely give her mine.

You'll give it, and not take a cake?
    Yes, that I will, I'm sure;
For see, she has but one leg got,
    And seems but very poor.

I'll give her mine, but take one cake,
    Miss Selfish quick repli'd;
But generous Mary said, Oh, no!
    I give her mine with pride.

Up to the girl they quickly got,
    And said, tell us how many
Of these nice little ginger-cakes
    You'll sell us for a penny?

I'll sell you six, she faintly said,
    For I am very poor;
They being good, I can't afford
    To sell you any more.

The gen'rous Mary's heart was fill'd,
    Do take this penny, friend?
I'll take no cakes, though mother gave
    This penny for to spend.

I'll give you mine, then, Sarah said,
    And only take one cake;
They look so nice, but any more
    I really will not take.

The little cripple eyed them both,
    Accept my thanks, I pray;
And if you're not in any haste,
    With me one moment stay.

I have five brothers now at home,
    My father he is dead;
My mother she has been long sick,
    And's now confin'd to bed.

I bring these ginger-cakes to sell,
    And they are very good;
At night I take the money home,
    And with it purchase food.

I am a cripple, as you see,
    My leg it mortified:
It was cut off—could say no more,
    Sobs choak'd her as she sigh'd.

The sisters left her and went on,
    Grew careless of their flowers;
Then Mary said, we'll see again
    That girl—Oh, gracious powers!

Poor cripple—oh, thy fate is hard,
    I can't forget thy sigh;
Lord, look upon that crippl'd child,
    In mercy from on high.

Thoughtful—grateful—home they went,
    But Sarah quite asham'd,
Because she took one cake—she begg'd
    It never might be nam'd.

Mary, the generous Mary, sigh'd,
    And feelingly replied,
I never in my life have felt
    More sweetly satisfied.

How thankful, sister, we should be,
    We have our limbs and food;
Our father and our mother lives,
    And we have every good.

Oh ! gracious heaven, hear my pray'r,
    Thy blessings shed abroad;
I'm thankful the poor crippl'd girl
    Was trav'ling in our road.

THE DEATH OF A FATHER.

Oh, fatal stroke !—must hope expire,
    And shall my tender parent die ?
The ghastly monarch, with charg'd quiver,
    Points his poniard—mocks my cry.

Father, does his arrows pierce thee ?
    Reclines thy heart against its wall;
Faint and trembling art thou sinking,
    Tastes thy lips the bitter'd gall ?

Does thy weaken'd fabric tremble—
    Will the grave my parent hide ?
Oh ! the stroke—I cannot bear it,
    Must I lose my tenderest guide.

Father ! tell me, art thou dying ?
    Lingers yet thy quivering breath:
Is the foe the conquest gaining,
    Must thou yield to conq'ring death ?

Thy eye-balls sinking in their sockets,
    Closing, shut to ope' no more:
Thy spirit quits its falling temple,
    Quits to seek another shore.

This hour robs me of my father,
    New-born troubles rise to birth:
Fatherless, and unprotected,
    Cold he sinks to mother earth.

Floods of tears, could you relieve me,
    Surely I'd relief obtain;
But, oh ! my breaking heart assures me,
    You can't assuage—tears flow in vain.

Chill'd is my prospect—let me linger
    Let me wash thy sacred bier
With those tears I would deposit
    In the grave with thee, dear sire.

Greedy grave—respite thy victim,
    Suspend thy yawnings while I weep;
Take thy little infant mourner,
    Let me with my father sleep.

Oh, the sexton's delving weapon
    Shows no pity to a child;
Thy steel is polish'd with the ashes
    Of death's victims—Oh, I'm wild !

O, how cruel !—death has seiz'd him,
    And the grave's cold bosom yawns
To receive her cold deposit,
    Chills my hopes, and sinks as dawns.

Heaven pardon, if I murmur,
    'Tis a child whose father's dead;
And the turf now hides its parent,
    All its hopes with him are fled.

Children, prize a tender father,
    Best protectors of the young;
Never let your conduct grieve them,
    Never vex them with your tongue.

THE WATCHMAN.

COLD was the night—the clock struck ten,
When lustily cried faithful Ben,
  The watchman of the street:
The wind blew rough, and chimnies fell,
He cried the hour, and cried it well,
  As fell the cutting sleet.

The pelting storm increased fast,
As poor old Ben was going past
  My father's kitchen-door:
For mercies' sake, my father cried,
As soon as he Ben's lanthorn spied,
  Step in, don't mind the floor.

It is a dreadful night, said Ben,
And when it will be fair again
  I really do not know:
For signs and chimnies fly about,
The rain o'erflows the turret's spout
  Into the streets below.

My father shook his head, and said,
Well, Ben, you hardly earn your bread;
  Tell me, are you no trade?
Ben, hesitating, said, I'm not,
A little learning, Sir, I've got,
  He sigh'd as thus he said·

I had a handsome fortune left,
But of a guide by death bereft,
  My father died;—and I

Gave unrestrain'd indulgence vent,
And very soon to ruin went,
  Which remedy defy.

Fool that I was—I'm now poor Ben,
Must wander through the streets from ten,
  Till peeps the morning's dawn:
A parent knows not his child's fate,
But should restrain 'ere its too late,
  Or keens the piercing thorn.

If children would but learn from me,
And from extravagance would flee,
  And mind the golden rule:
That child who does his money spend,
To vain pursuits his time will lend,
  I call that child a fool.

The gale it ceas'd, and Ben withdrew,
Just as the clock was striking two,
  I heard his lusty voice:
You are a watchman, true, thought I
(I thought of Ben, and heav'd a sigh,)
  Compell'd, and not from choice.

Children should watch their actions well,
And never let gay notions dwell,
  Or occupy their mind:
But straight pursue the path that's right,
And follow good with all their might,
  The advantages they will find.

SCHOOL.

CHILDREN are sent to school to learn,
  And diligent should be;
Then their improvement will shine forth,
  And all will plainly see,
That they are good, and friends will praise;
  Their parents will caress
The child who diligently tries
  Sound learning to possess.

Abundant cause for gratitude
  Have children, who are taught
At School to read, to spell, and write,
  And are from ign'rance brought.

What is a child, unlearnt, untaught,
  His mind is wild and vague;
A book is seal'd—his vacant time
  Is irksome and a plague.

What better than poor Afric's son,
  Or savage of the wood,
Who wildly run thro' deserts, moors,
  To join the chase of blood?

A VISIT TO NEWGATE.

The Father of two little boys,
   Resolved one day to take
A walk through Newgate with the lads,
   Just for example's sake:

One of these boys was very good,
   The other the reverse;
A pilfering little petty thief,
   Was stubborn and perverse.

The father's fears would oft pourtray
   The little rascal's end;
If he was not reclaim'd, and soon,
   And did his conduct mend.

Come, Jack, the father said, you'll see
   What thieving does my lad;
This prison's built thus strong to keep
   The wicked and the bad.

The outer door turns on its hinge,
   The massive bars between;
And through the gratings of the cells,
   The inmates faintly seen.

'Twas here the voice of sorrow struck
   Th' affrighted ear of all;
The clinking chains, the frenzied yell,
   The harden'd culprit's bawl.

But learning curbs the wand'ring mind,
   It chases nature's night;
Affords a mental feast, and gives
   A soul-reviving light.

Prize, children, prize your book while young,
   Anticipate your school;
When you've a chance to learn, and not,
   You ought to die a fool.

Children who neglect to learn,
   Give evidence they're bad;
What must a tender parent feel,
   Whose son is such a lad !

Such children must be whipt and scourg'd,
   They don't deserve to eat;
For 'tis the diligent alone
   Are worthy of their meat.

Contrast a child that's good, with one
   Who hates his book and school;
What picture does the blockhead give,
   But that he is a fool ?

Then view the diligent and good,
   The child whose willing mind
Is bent on learning—ever tries
   To seek, the prize—he'll find.

Confin'd within a grated cell,
   A little boy they spy'd,
With nothing but a crust to eat,
   All other food denied.

For why this little boy put here ?
   For thieving you must know;
And there are many more beside,
   In lock-ups down below.

The little urchin's meagre face
   Was moisten'd with his tears;
The dread of punishment had rous'd
   His keen foreboding fears.

His parents he at first would rob,
   Then after bolder grew;
Stole trifles first, then grasp'd at all,
   Or any thing in view.

Exploring still the vaulted maze,
   Some dismal sobs assail'd
Their nerve-drawn ears—'twas grief, alas !
   Repentance unavail'd.

The sighs were shuddering exiles' cast
   To echo 'long the walls,
Repeating chill'd responses hoarse,
   And mock'd the victim's calls.

'Twas some poor men, who, doom'd to die
   Upon the coming day,
Were venting frantic tears of grief,
   And kneeling down to pray.

This was matur'd full-grown crime,
   Its end, and its reward;
Reproaches in full stature stood,
   And death to fainting aw'd.

Come, Children, view the march of crime,
   Exploring shun the road;
" Steal not at all," your Maker says,
   Such is the law of God.

THE ORPHANS.

PETER, walking with his mother,
Spy'd an orphan, with her brother,
Going about to sell their matches,
With shoeless feet and clad in patches.

Their looks bespoke that they were poor,
Their modest calls, from door to door,
Laid claim to pity—told their grief,
And crav'd in eloquence—relief.

Peter, whose tender heart was fired,
Ran t'wards the orphans, and enquir'd,
If they were hungry—wanted meat ?
And if they had not, ought to eat.

Have you no father, mother, friend ?
I've got this sixpence for to spend;
If it will do you any good,
Take it, and buy yourselves some food.

But tell me, first of all, I pray,
Do you sell matches every day ?
And don't the stones wound your poor feet,
While walking through the paved street ?

The sister orphan, sick and wan,
Sigh'd gratitude—and thus began
Her undisguised tale of woe,
And why they wander'd to and fro ?

" Kind-hearted sir, our parents' dead,
" With them our 'lone support has fled;
" We are from Scotland: here we have
" No friend to succour or to save.

" These matches that we have, we try
" To sell—but seldom people buy;
" They'll drive us from their very door,
" Because we're ragged and so poor.

"Sometimes a feeling heart we meet,
"While wandering on from street to street;
"But seldom do we ever find
"A soul like your's, so generous, kind."

She courtesied, sigh'd, as thus she spoke,
Her bitter sobs did utterance choke,
Which noble Peter kindly eyed.
And try'd to sooth, at length she cried,

"Bear with my weakness, tender friend,
"And if you can five minutes spend,
"I will unfold to you our woe,
"Our cause of wandering to and fro.

"My father had a roving mind,
"Took us abroad, in hopes to find
"A place where we could live in pleasure,
"And amass a world of treasure.

"But, ah, alas! hard cruel fate
"Decreed to us this uncouth state;
"My father's hopes were blighted sore,
"Which left us destitute and poor.

"Resolv'd again to venture home,
"Resolv'd no more again to roam;
"To work our passage home he try'd,
"We sail'd, but, oh! my parents died.

"The ocean is my parents' grave,
"And we, alas! no parents have;
"We wander now about with matches,
"Poor orphans—clad in rags and patches.

"Sometimes unto the rich we go,
"And venture to the door below;
"But full-fed servants often say,
"We want no matches—go away.

"Oh, cruel fate!"—she heav'd a sob,
And Peter's heart with union throb;
Strove hard to sooth their bitter fears,
The three gave vent, and mingled tears.

They sigh'd, shook hands, and bid adieu,
And Peter watch'd them while in view;
At home he told his tale as willing,
His father gave to him a shilling.

Children, who know no want of food,
Whose parents are both kind and good;
Think on the orphans' selling matches,
Be thankful you're not clad in patches.

Yes! prize your homes and milder state,
Think on the orphans' coarser fate;
Be grateful—and give God the praise,
He deals with you in milder ways.

A VISIT TO THE BLIND ASYLUM.

Oh! what a blessing is the sight,
The sense of vision and of light,
To view the rising sun at morn,
And see the gilded sky at dawn.
Survey the beauties nature grants,
The varied colours that she paints;
To tread with safety on the way,
Enjoy illumined summer's day.
Discern approaching dangers nigh,
Or contemplate a starry sky;
Enjoy the pleasures of a book,
And on its pleasing pages look.
Such pleasures do our sight afford,
And God once said, "the light was good."

Yes, gratitude gave birth to thought,
As swiftly she her lessons taught,
When visiting the School for Blind,
'Twas there these thoughts rush'd on my mind.

Lord, what a picture this I see,
For why, indulgent Lord, why me?
Blest with the sense of vision clear,
The paths of life to smooth and cheer.

What is it that my eyes behold?
The healthy, young, and wrinkled old,
Shut up, poor souls, in gloomy night,
Walking without one ray of light.

Come, child, I'll take you by the hand,
And lead you through the gloomy band;
See, there, a man a basket making,
A woman, too, her wheel is taking:
Some making whips, some in their looms,
All hands are busy in their rooms;
Some highly-gifted we shall find,
But, ah, alas ! they are quite blind.

Children, mix pity with surprise,
Be grateful that you have good eyes;
Your mercies great—give God the praise,
He deals with you in milder ways.

THE DEATH OF A MOTHER.

SUPPORTED by the yielding pillow,
   The tender Mother sat in bed,
With her children weeping round her,
   With list'ning ears at what she said.

She faintly utter'd—" My children,
   " Soon I must leave you, little dears;
" Now I feel death's hand upon me,
   " But don't distress me with your tears.

" The mandate's issued, I must leave you,
   " You feel the summons cruel, dears;
" Death with hasty strides approaches,
   " Life's curtain draws—a new world appears

" Soon your mother will be lifeless,
   " For you I'd wish but to be spar'd;
" Ah, why this wish, I ne'er shall have it,
   " Never see my children rear'd.

" Submit then nobly, what's appointed,
   " 'Tis the unerring will of Heaven;
" 'Tis God who summons up your Mother,
   " 'Tis He who has the mandate given.

" May God protect you, infant darlings,
   " Take my blessing from my heart;
" Oh ! I feel death's arrow piercing,
   " I fall the victim of his dart."

Thus sunk the tender dying mother,
   While her children wept around,
And survey'd her pallid visage,
   While life's yielding cords unbound.

Life had fled—her frame was cooling,
   Oh ! the sobs, the infants' sigh;
Weeping statues—breaking silence,
   Weeping, asks the question, why ?

Why, oh, death ! select our Mother,
   When we needed most her care;
Could not thy cruel hand have spar'd her—
   Could'st thou not our Mother spare ?

Oh ! this day—a day of sorrow,
   Clad in sable mourning's dress;
Now the cruel monarch's emblems
   Feeds on infantine distress.

Tears moisten the mould that covers
   Her dear remains from our eye,
While her happy spirit hovers
   Round her children, ever nigh.

Who could bear to see them weeping,
   And not mingle one soft tear ?
Could you witness infants' crying
   O'er a loving mother's bier ?

Where's the child who thus refuses ?
   Or, while weeping—grateful prove,
That their Mother lives to succour,
   And are worthy Parents' love.

A VISIT TO THE LUNATIC ASYLUM.

COME child with me, a father said,
I often have a visit paid
To yon receptacle of woe,
For Lunatics.—Come, child, and know,
And prize the blessing you possess,

And prove the feeling you profess.
Come, shed a tear o'er those devoid
Of what you have through life enjoy'd:
See, in this mansion of distress,
The throngs of those who don't possess
Their reason; but with constant moan
Cast ashes on her vacant throne;
Her sceptre cankering in the dust,
Fair reason weeping o'er the rust;
Her seat deserted, fallen, decay,
And midnight horrors shade fair day.
Reason, thy grateful cheering light
Entomb'd 'neath ashes, clad in night,
Lays prostrate—where thy being's ceas'd,
Thy sons are levell'd with the beast.

What means that horrid dreadful yell,
Those screeches from yon grated cell;
The frightful clinking of the chain,
And wild effusions of the brain?

How madly now he tears his hair,
What wildness mixes with his stare;
With rage he rends his tatter'd clothes,
More vicious and still stronger grows.
What awful wreathings vent in rage,
With eye-balls starting, dread presage;
My God! can creature man thus sink,
Plung'd headlong down th' appalling brink.

Point out the man who grateful shows
That he the worth of reason knows;
That he his reason holds from God,
And stays by gratitude the rod
That might afflict—that might chastise—
The man who does the gift despise.

Were reason's channels choak'd and dried,
You of her benefits denied;
Read here what you would surely be,
Your picture in these inmates see.

Who could withhold a grateful heart,
For the possession of that part
Which lifts the mortal from the beast?
Yes, gratitude it claims at least.

But, oh! possessor ever know,
If gratitude you'd truly show,
Let every reasoning power be given
Up to the service of kind Heav'n.

IDLENESS.

An idle child is e'er despis'd,
  And don't deserve its meat;
Good children, never wish the bread
  Of Idleness to eat.

An idle girl, or idle boy,
  Is hated as a pest;
Like dirty pigs, they always love
  In slothfulness to rest.

An idle child is never loved,
　Will follow other's vice;
And those who do this vice indulge
　Is never very nice.

They're thrice more wicked and more vile,
　In robberies and theft;
From step to step they go, their end
　Is misery and death.

For Idleness, it ever did,
　And ever will betray;
It is the devil's cunning bait,
　T'ensnare, and then to slay.

It is a sin God ever hates,
　And good men do despise;
God ever did, and always will,
　This wickedness chastise.

Then, children, ever cultivate
　An indust'rous active mind;
A blessing it will always prove,
　And the reward you'll find.

Politeness—often misapplied,
Worn on the fancy—but belied;
Martyred or prostituted grace,
Attempted mimicks in unmeaning face.

Politeness—thou art oft misused,
As often is they name abused;
Thou'rt not about the coxcomb seen,
Nor yet confin'd to prince or queen.

Thou'rt found sometimes amongst the poor,
And seen to grace the cottage-door;
Thy fixt abode is common sense,
Which adds a grace to elegance.

Children who thy smiles invite,
Who wish and try to be polite,
Will never suddenly intrude,
And always shudder to be rude:

Will not say much—but when they speak,
Will neither shout, speak low, nor squeak,
Be easy, modest, free from fright,
The child does this is quite polite.

ON POLITENESS.

Politeness—little understood,
It means in children to be good;
A modest, gentle, carriage, free
From those pratlings that we see.

A VISIT TO CHELSEA COLLEGE.

Good children ought to be indulg'd,
　So William's father thought;
As such, to Chelsea College he
　Once little William brought.

The little fellow quite amaz'd
　When got within the gate;
The building and its inmates did
　His youthful mind elate.

He star'd about to feast his eyes,
　At last he silence broke,
To hear the pensioners' long tales,
　Their merry cracking joke:

" Father," the little fellow said,
　" How happy they appear;
" They joke, and laugh, and look so clean,
　" And give a welcome cheer.

" Why some are blind, and some have lost
　" A leg, and some an arm;
" Why all these amputations, Sir,
　" From whence arose their harm ? "

His Father smil'd at his remarks,
　And really well he might;
He seem'd to think, to get a birth
　He'd have to lose his sight.

"William, these maimed men are fed,
  "And want for no good thing;
"For they have fought their country's wars,
  "As soldiers of their King.

"And Britons never suffer those
  "Who fought and victory won,
"To wander friendless when got maim'd,
  "But shields them as a son."

A Briton's heart must beat with joy,
  Whene'er that Briton eyes
This generous monument of pride,
  That all the world outvies.

May Briton's blood flow in thy veins,
  A Briton's heart possess;
May you true British feeling show,
  Which feeling you profess.

Britain's exalted by her arms,
  But what exalts her most,
Is generous feeling !—may this be
  Ever a Briton's boast.

We have a thousand reasons why
  We should a tribute bring,
Of gratitude to God—and shout,
  God save our gracious King.

A BRAVE BOY

During the campaign in Caraccas, a boy appeared in the tent of Morillo, overwhelmed in tears. The chief desired to be informed for what purpose he was there. The child said he came to beg the life of his father, then a prisoner in Morillo's camp. "What can you do to save your father?" asked the general. "I can do but little," said the boy; "but what I can do, shall be done." Morillo seized the little fellow's ear,—"Would you suffer your ear to be taken off, to obtain your father's liberty?" demanded he. "I certainly would," was the answer. A soldier was accordingly ordered to cut off the ear by pieces. The boy wept, but resisted not. "Would you lose your other ear, for the accomplishment of your purpose?" was the next question. "I have suffered much, but I can still suffer," replied the boy. The other ear was taken off by one stroke of the knife. "And now," said Morillo, "depart, the father of such a son is dangerous to Spain— he must pay the forfeit of his life." The maimed child was passed from the quarters of the general to witness the execution of his father !

MEMOIRS

OF

THE LITTLE MAN

AND

THE LITTLE MAID:

WITH

SOME INTERESTING PARTICULARS OF THEIR LIVES.

NEVER BEFORE PUBLISHED.

London:

PUBLISHED BY B. TABART,
AT THE JUVENILE AND SCHOOL LIBRARY, NO. 157,
NEW BOND-STREET.
1807.

There was a little man,
And he woed a little maid,
And he said, " Little maid,
    Will you wed, wed, wed ?
I have little more to say
Than will you, aye or nay ?
For the least said
    Is soonest amended, ded."

The little maid replied,
" Should I be your little bride,
Pray what shall we have
    For to eat, eat, eat ?
Will the flame you're only rich in
Light a fire in the kitchen,
Or the little god of love
    Turn the spit, spit, spit ? "

The little man replied,
And some say a little cried,
For his little heart was big
    With sorrow, sorrow, sorrow,
" My offers are but small,
But you have my little all,
And what we have not got
    We must borrow, borrow, borrow."

The little man thus spoke,
His heart was almost broke,
And all for the sake
  Of her charms, charms, charms;
The little maid relents,
And, softened, she consents
The little man to take
  To her arms, arms, arms.

The little maid's consent
Obtained, to church they went,
Where the parson joined their hands
  With pleasure, pleasure, pleasure.
With rapture now he eyed
His blooming little bride,
His all! his house and lands!
  His treasure, treasure, treasure!

They passed their days and nights
In pleasure and delights
In feasting, mirth, and play,
  And dancing, dancing, dancing:
The little maid, they say,
Tripped merrily away,
With her little man so gay,
  Lightly prancing, prancing, prancing.

The honey-moon soon over,
No more a flaming lover,
The little man repents
  Of his folly, folly, folly;
His little cash had fled,
While he droops his pensive head,
And in sighs his sorrow vents,
  A prey to melancholy.

The little maid grew bold,
She would rant and she would scold,
And call her little man
  A great oaf, oaf, oaf.
He wished the deuce would take her:
While the butcher or the baker
Would not trust him for a chop,
  Or a loaf, loaf, loaf.

The little man reflected,
His little means neglected,
Would serve but to increase
  His sorrow, sorrow, sorrow;
To his little wife he cried,
" Let us lay our feuds aside,
And endeavour to provide
  For to-morrow, morrow, morrow."

His little wife repented,
To his wishes she consented,
And said she could work
   With her needle, needle, needle.
The little man was not idle,
He played upon the fiddle,
And he earned a good living
   With his tweedle, tweedle, tweedle.

To the little man's great joy,
He soon had a little boy,
Which made his little heart
   Quite glad, glad, glad.
'Twas the little mother's pleasure
To nurse her little treasure,
Which rapture did impart
   To his dad, dad, dad.

Now every thing was smiling,
There was no more reviling,
While chearful plenty crowned
   Their labours, labours, labours.
The little man with joy,
Would take his little boy,
And shew him all around
   To his neighbours, neighbours, neighbours.

Whittington and His Cat

Who has not heard of Whittington,
Thrice Lord Mayor of London Town ?
In former times, (for long ago
Lived Whittington, as records show,)
Poor country lads were often told
That London streets were paved with gold.
One day, as Dick upon the grass
Reclined, a waggon chanced to pass
To London Bound : this thought occurr'd—
I'll see if all is true I've heard :
So jumping up, away he ran,
1. And walk'd beside the waggon-man.
Judge Richard's feelings of surprise,
When London really met his eyes !
Not yet by sad experience taught,
His mind was fix'd in pleasing thought.
His friend the waggoner pass'd on ;
Poor Whittington was left alone ;
That night was houseless. In the morn,
The youthful wanderer rose forlorn :
Exhausted, spiritless and faint,
The poor lad utter'd no complaint ;
But, weeping, stretch'd himself before
A wealthy Merchant's open door.
The portly Cook, who lived at ease
And slighted Richard's miseries,
Bade him depart, with angry face,
And seek another resting place.
Just at this moment to his home
The worthy master chanced to come :
2. " Why lie you there, my lad ? " said he,
" Labour you do not like, I see."
" I never would," was Dick's reply,
" Thus idly on your door-steps lie,
Could I but work obtain. I'm weak,
And vainly for employment seek."
" Get up, poor fellow ; let me see—
Go, help them in the scullery."
Soon as the morning sun arose,
Dick quickly to the kitchen goes
To ply his task ; and though the Cook
Oft greeted him with sullen look,

He still determined to obey,
And sought to please her every way.
Yet still she scolded, still would try
To make him from her service fly ;
Nay more, she sometimes took a broom,
3. And beat poor Richard round the room ;
But Whittington, as Christian should,
Always requited ill with good.
Within the room where Richard slept,
The rats and mice a revel kept ;
And nightly as he lay in bed,
They ran across his face and head :
Among such plagues the attempt was vain
Refreshing sleep or rest to gain.
Yet patient Dick did not repine,
He made his master's slippers shine.
The merchant's eye his labour traced :
And finding kindness rightly placed,
Sent him a penny by the maid,—
Industry always is repaid.
4. With this poor Richard bought a Cat,
Dire enemy to mouse and rat.
Puss went to work that very night,
5. And put the rats and mice to flight.
The Merchant had an only child,
A daughter affable and mild,
6. From whom poor Richard learn'd to read.
Slowly indeed did he proceed ;
But those who readily pursue
The proper path, may wonders do.
Just like the snail, which seldom fails
To reach the top of garden-rails,
Because with diligence its race
Continues till it gains the place.
The merchant summon'd to the hall
His clerks and servants, one and all,
Told of his Ship, and then explain'd
How wealth was by her cargo gain'd ;
To fill the white and spreading sail,
His Captain waited for a gale ;
Then ask'd if each would like to send
Something which might to profit tend.

1

4

2

5

3

6

7

10

8

11

9

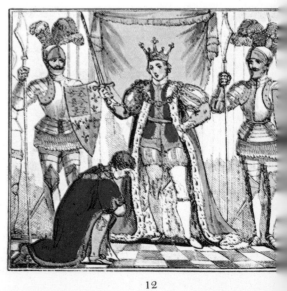

12

All but young Richard heard with joy
This kind proposal ; he, poor boy !
Stood mute and mournful. " Why so sad ?
Hast nothing for a venture, lad ? "
" No, Sir," in downcast tone he said,—
" Only a Cat, Sir, over-head."

7. " Well, bring the Cat, my lad ; let's see
How fortunate poor Puss may be."
Dick wept his tabby friend to lose ;
His grief served others to amuse.
All ask'd him if his famous Cat
Would catch a fine gold mouse or rat ?
Or whether for enough 'twould sell
To buy a stick to beat him well ?
At last poor Richard's temper fail'd,
And anger for a time prevail'd :
For all he did or tried to do,
Still worse and worse Cook's conduct grew.
Darkness had scarcely pass'd away,
On the morning of All-Hallows day,
When from the house he turn'd to go
With heavy heart and footsteps slow.
His future path unknown, he sigh'd ;
For all was new and yet untried.
To Holloway he walk'd, when, lo !
He heard the merry bells of Bow :
In Richard's ear they seem'd to chime
This uncouth, strange, and simple rhyme :

8. " Turn again, Whittington,
" Thrice Lord Mayor of London."
Mayor of London !—can there be
Such honour yet design'd for me ?
To London Dick return'd before
His tyrant oped the kitchen door.
The Merchant's ship, by weather tost,
Was driven on the Barbary Coast.
The Monarch of that distant land
Had hourly visits from a band
Of puny thieves—even rats and mice,
Who ate up all things sweet and nice.
The Captain offer'd Dicky's Cat,

9. Which snapp'd up every mouse and rat.
" Now," said the King, " cost what it may,
That creature must not go away,
But for the Cat I'll give you more
Than for the rest of all your store."
And so he did ; and bags of gold
Upon the carpet they behold.
Which quickly to the ship convey'd,
Most nobly for poor Pussy paid.
The Captain back to England came,

The herald of Dick's wealth and fame.
I need not say, to all he'd send
To share his wealth, to all a friend.
The cross Cook even was not forgot,
Now Heaven had so improved his lot ;
And numbers bless'd the happy hour
Which gave poor Richard wealth and power.

10. The Merchant wishing Richard joy,
Said, " May you, simple honest boy,
Be happy ! May you ever be
Famed for your strict integrity ! "
Sheriff of London he was made,
And in his new career display'd
Manners so mild yet dignified,
So free from forwardness and pride,
That all the Corporation said
He must an Alderman be made.
In this high office praise he earn'd,
And shortly after was return'd
Lord Mayor of London : then he told
What once he thought the bells foretold.
He thrice the Civic honour gain'd,
And each time general praise obtain'd.
When the heroic Henry came
Fresh from the well-fought field of fame,
In City chronicles we find,
With Whittington the Monarch dined.

11. The gentle Emma now became
A blooming bride to grace his name,
To bless his fireside hours, and share
The honours of the great Lord Mayor.
Let every Child who reads this tale,
Remember Virtue cannot fail
To be beloved : that Wealth cannot
Confer true glory on our lot ;
And that respect and love outweigh
The idle pleasures of a day :
That none on poverty should frown,
Nor on an honest man look down,
Since every virtue may adorn
The being whom you treat with scorn,
And none to wealth or rank can say,
" Ye cannot, shall not flee away."
To make his glory yet more bright,

12. Our Whittington was dubb'd a Knight.
Sir Richard fully understood
The pure delight of doing good ;
Rejoiced to succour the oppress'd,
And aid the humble and distress'd
A life in constant virtue spent,
Became his proudest monument.

Nursery Morals

My little Ellen,

Your beloved Brother's life was taken from him, on the same day of the month, on the same hour of the day, that your life was given to you.

Oh! may you live to bring those virtues to perfection, which, in him, bloomed so fair and promising; which, in him, were so early crushed. Yet not crushed—but transplanted.

Had be lived, I had not needed to write of youthful virtue. His life would have shown it to you, in all its loveliness.

But he is gone!

And we can now only think upon what he was—what he would have been.

Happy if, in imitating his virtues, we insure his calm and smiling death.

My little Ellen,

The inheritor of your precious Brother's life, and faintly bearing a resemblance in form, and feature, and character,—

The same blue eye,

The same arch smile,

The same buoyant step,

The same intelligent glance;

May the same virtue be also yours.

Your doating, but unconsoled, and inconsolable Mother,

THE AUTHOR.

London, 1818.

THE PIG.

How we all turn with scorn from that Pig. His skin is thick in dirt.

He lies on damp, musty straw, and rolls in mud and mire.

He lives to eat and drink, and will perhaps die, because he is too fat.

How sad to look on so dirty a brute.

But, oh! how much more sad to be like him. To eat all day long.

To eat much more than ought to be eaten, And to be sick with greediness.

Then to lie down in the dirt, and sleep in the mud.

This is all most shocking.

Boys and girls are not quite so bad.

But, sometimes, they are *almost* as bad.

Have you not seen children devour sweets and delicacies without end?

Tarts, and cakes, and fruits?

Then, with greasy face and dirty hands, fall asleep on the ground.

Their clothes all spoiled.

Their limbs all twisted.

Well, are not such children as bad as Pigs? Aye, and worse, much worse.

For they know better,

They have the choice to be clean, if they please. We can all wash ourselves when we chuse.

We can keep our clothes neat and tight.

We should scorn to be seen with hair uncombed, and our dress in rags.

Girls can sew and mend the rents in their coats and frocks.

And take care to be at all times neat,

Or else, in truth, they will be no better than the pigs we all look on with scorn.

SWEEP! SWEEP!

HARK! what weak voice is that which calls at my door?

It is cold, wet, and dark.

I shake with cold as I lie in my snug bed.

I look up at the dim light, and think it is not yet time to rise.

For it is raw and damp.

No fire is yet lit.

The room down stairs is not yet made neat and warm.

No urn is on the table,

No bread, no cream, no tea.

Breakfast is not ready.

I will not rise, I will lie still in my snug bed till all shall be fit for me below.

Hush! that voice sounds once more. Sweep! sweep!

I creep from my bed, and see the poor child that calls.

How small he is.

What weak limbs.

What bare feet.

How red are his hands with the cold.

How his head shakes with the cold.

A few tears are on his cheek, and make a white streak down the soot.

Who are you, poor boy?

Hark! he speaks.

I have no father, no mother, no friends.

But I have a master, a cruel master,

Who beats me, and starves me, and sends me up small dark flues.

One day I burnt my arm, but no one cared for my pain.

One day I fell down a long chimney and broke my leg.

But no one felt for me.

I have a wound in my side, but I have no salve to heal it.

You pity me, little girl!

But hush! I must not even hear the kind words of pity, for my master is near, and he will say I complain,

And he will beat me the more.

Oh! I cannot look upon this boy. His pains wring my heart.

Can nothing be done to save him, to ease him.

To snatch him from his hard, hard fate?

Little girl, dry your tears. I have some good news for you.

There will soon be a law, a blessed law, that shall stop the further pangs of the poor sweep.

A frame made of wood and horse-hair, and brass or iron chains, shall clear our flues, in the place of those wretched lads.

Nay, should the law not pass, I hope every body that has feeling, every body that pretends to have feeling, will persist in using the frame of wood instead of the poor boys.

Good Heaven! must we have laws to make us feel pity?

Can we not feel without a law to force us?

Do we call ourselves human, yet forget the rights of humanity?

I am a mother, and look upon my son.

He is clean, and healthy, and happy.

Joy is in his eye,

Smiles are on his lip

His voice is gay,

His steps are light.

He is glad, and makes me glad.

Oh! could I bear, for an instant, to think of his being a sweep.

Of his being in pain,

Sick, sad, friendless.

My heart bleeds at the thought. What must be that mother's pangs, who sees the fact?

God only knows; her sorrow must be too great for words, too great for me to paint.

Yet, why should her child be worse off than mine?

Why should he suffer because he is poor?

Suffer more than the son of the lord and the duke?

The rich man, the great man, would be wild with grief, if their sons were to be made to endure half the pains that thousands of climbing boys every day, every hour, endure.

Then in pity, in mercy, in duty, let every great and rich man,

Every lord and duke,

Join heart and hand to make this blessed law.

It might be, it has been, that the child of a great man, stolen from his home, has been sold to a sweep, and made a climbing boy.

Such a chance can only be prevented by this law.

How do I hope then that it will pass.

Since else both rich and poor, both great and lowly, will go on to risk the anguish of their children's sufferings.

And great will be the joy of many hearts, when those cruel Sweeps shall be forced to use frames in the place of boys.

We say cruel Sweeps,

But, truly, we are all as cruel as they, whilst we go on sending for boys to clean our flues.

When we can get frames of wood, by which the work can be done as well.

If it is more dear, sure no one would grudge a few pence to save a fellow-creature from aches and wounds.

I say, God bless the good man who brought this matter to a law.

SILLY JANE.

JANE was fair as the lily, and blithe as the lark.

She thought her bloom could never fade, and was vain of it.

She thought with scorn of those who were not so fair.

She called herself bright as the butterfly, and gay as the tulip.

Her mother led her into the garden, and showed her the butterfly dead.

The storm had crushed it to the ground.

It lay there soiled and cold.

A rude gale had passed over the tulip, and snapped the proud blossom from its stem.

Its once rich leaves lay spread on the damp earth.

The grubs were crawling upon it, the ants were feeding upon it.

Even such shall be the fate of the fairest face, when death shall lay it low in the dark grave.

Worms shall there defile the fairest cheek, and riot on the sweetest lip.

Look, Jane, and learn a moral from the scene before you.

But Jane was deaf to the voice of her mother.

She could have learnt, for who cannot ? But she would not learn.

She chose to go on in her own way.

In a little while, Jane was sick, and red spots broke out on her skin.

How sad were her thoughts, how full of pain her fancies !

Her complaint was mild, but the fear of losing her beauty made it severe to Jane.

Other girls had the same disease, but no one

so badly as Jane; for no one, like Jane, thought on the chance of having a red skin and a spoiled face.

Jane became well again; her face was not spoiled, her skin was as fair as before:

And Jane grew more vain, and thought, as she had escaped one chance, she should escape every chance, and that her bloom would never fade.

Many people are as foolish as Jane, and fancy chance may hurt every one but themselves.

But Jane found there was one foe to beauty that she could not shun.

She found she could not help growing old.

Each year took something from her charms.

Wrinkles crossed her brow.

A yellow hue took place of the white of her cheek.

Her hair lost its bright gloss, and a few grey curls were seen round her neck.

What was to be done?

Jane tried strange washes to bleach her skin; they made it more brown.

Her teeth, one by one, fell out of her head.

The fair blithe Jane found herself an old woman.

With grey hairs, a long chin, and hollow cheeks.

"That it should come to this!" she would say with sighs and tears.

Why mourn, Jane? Did you not wish to live?

And can you live without growing old?

Would you have wished to die early, in your first bloom, with all your charms fresh and bright?

Even in that case, you would, by this time, have faded in the grave, and have been food for worms.

Fair maids! there is but one kind of charm that never fades—the charm of the mind, the charm of virtue, which is as lovely in age as in youth.

KIND TOM.

I was glad to mark Tom, one day, when he was in a shop, and thought no one saw him.

A weak wan child, in rags, came to the door and begged for a penny.

Tom had a smart whip in his hand, which he was fond of, and meant to buy.

It would cost all the pence in his hand—All the pence that he had.

Tom cast a sad look at the sick child.

Her face was pale, and wet with tears.

Some tears came into Tom's eyes too, and some good thoughts into Tom's heart.

"I will buy a plain whip!" he said, and put down the smart one.

The man of the shop did not see the pale girl; he was cross, and told Tom, with a frown, that he was a bad lad, to change his mind just when he was about to pay for the whip.

Tom's heart told him he was not bad, for his cause of changing was a good one:

So he bore the man's frown,

And chose a plain whip,

And saved half his pence.

And oh! with what joy he threw those pence into the thin hands of the beggar-girl.

She bade "God bless the good, good boy."

And Tom felt her blessing warm in his heart.

For it was gay!—oh! how gay!

The chink of the pence, as they fell into the hand of the girl, made the cross shopman look that way.

He saw her, and knew why Tom had changed his mind.

He felt shame for his own harsh speech; he felt love for the act of Tom.

But Tom did not know that any eye saw his deed.

That any voice praised it.

He was glad to do good,

And found his own pleased thoughts a rich reward.

If we do any act, only for the sake of praise, What good is it?

It is like working for hire, or toiling for a certain payment.

There can be no merit in such things, and our hearts will blame, rather than praise us, for being good only for what may be said of us—

For being good for what may be thought of us.

This is not goodness, this is vanity: and vanity is folly.

Some folks, when they perform a kind act, are looking for some return.

How mean is this! How weak! how selfish!

Is it not selfish to do good in hopes of a return?

And can any thing that is selfish be generous?

No, it is not possible.

A boy helps his playmate, not from kindness, but because he expects his playmate will help him.

" I will not eat Dick's nuts," says Joe, " because I shall have some reward for my not eating them."

Ann weeds Kate's garden, and is thinking all the rest of the day what reward she shall get for her pains.

Now these children are plainly thinking of themselves, not of their friends.

They are truly selfish:

And, worst of all, they are selfish under the plea of being generous.

Oh! I do not love such tricks.

I could find it in my heart to say, oh! I hate such tricks.

No, my dear little ones, do good for the love of goodness, and ask no praise.

Be kind to those you love, because you love them, not that they may in turn be kind to you.

But if you act from love, trust that they also will act from love.

And be thankful that you have the power to please and to oblige.

It may happen that those we serve may some day serve us.

But I tell you, for a truth, that this does not often happen.

I will say, that it very seldom happens.

Therefore, I tell you this, that you may not deceive yourselves with hopes of what you will not come to pass.

For who is it we ought most to serve?

The poor, the weak, the sick.

These can have small chance of repaying us for what we do for them.

Yet these are the people who most need our help.

Were we to gain the habit of thinking who can, and who cannot, return our service, we should serve the great and the rich alone.

We should not serve the widow, the orphan, and those who have no helper.

And would this be just?

Would this be kind?

I leave it to your own hearts to answer me.

The Child's Book on the Soul

A LETTER

To little Boys and Girls, from one who hopes they will learn, both how to be good, and to do good. For, to be good, and to do good, is the only way to be happy.

MY DEAR CHILDREN

I HAVE six children. They are all quite young; and the eldest is not nine years of age. They often ask me to tell them stories; and I am glad to do so, when they are good children, and do what their father and mother wish to have them do. I wrote this book for them, and I have read it to the three eldest. The others are too young to understand it yet, but I hope they will be able to do so when they grow older.

I thought it might do other little boys and girls good to read this book, or to have it read to them. So I have had it printed; and, I hope, my Dear Children, that it will do *you good*, to learn and understand what I have written. If you cannot read it easily, you can get somebody to read it to you, and to tell you the meaning of any hard words which you do not understand.

I shall tell you a story about a little boy and his mother. The mother will say a great many things to the little boy, and he will say a great many things to his mother.

The mother we will call Mrs. Stanhope: and the little boy, her son, we will call Robert.

I do not know, that there were ever such persons, as Mrs. Stanhope and Robert; but I can tell you better what I wish to tell you, if I talk about a mother and her son, and if I give them both names.

Do not be in a hurry to get to the end of the story. Be attentive to every part of it. If you should not understand any word, or any thing which Mrs. Stanhope and Robert say to each other, be sure to ask somebody to explain it to you. This is the way, you should always do, when you find any thing hard in the books which you read. It will not do you any good to read books, if you do not understand them.

And when your father or mother, or any body is talking with you, and you do not know what they mean,—tell them you do not understand them, and ask them to please to explain it to you.

And when they try to explain any thing to you, or to tell you the meaning of any hard words, and you do not still quite understand them, do not be afraid to tell them so. *It is very wrong, to say that you understand a thing, when you do not.*

Try to understand every thing that you are reading, or learning, or that any body says to you, and then you will improve fast; and then you will become wise, and I hope also, good and happy.

But I suppose, you would like to hear the story about Mrs. Stanhope and her son Robert, which, I hope, will be both instructive and entertaining to you.

I am your friend,

THOMAS H. GALLAUDET.

ROBERT STANHOPE was five years old. His father died when Robert was a little boy. His mother had one other child, Eliza, who was three years old.

They lived in a pleasant town, in a small white house, near the church and the school-house.

Robert and Eliza did not go to school. Their mother said they should go when they were a little older. She used to teach them at home. She was a very kind mother, and they both loved her very much.

One evening, Robert put Mrs. Stanhope in mind, that she promised to talk with him about the soul. She said she would do so, after Eliza had gone to bed; and told Robert to sit down in his little chair, and study a short lesson, while she went up stairs with his sister. Robert was a good boy and did as his mother bade him, and when she came down, she took a chair and sat by him, and they had the following conversation.

MOTHER. Robert, can you tell me what the soul is ?

ROBERT. *My soul*, mother, *is that something inside of me which thinks.*

M. You have a body and a soul. I have a body and a soul. Eliza has a body and a soul. And every man, and woman, and boy, and girl, has a body and a soul.

R. Mother, have very little babies souls ?

M. Yes, my son, but you know they do not think much, till they grow older.

R. Mother, does the soul grow ?

M. Not like the body. But the soul is able to think more and more; and to understand more and more; and to learn more and more; and to know more and more a great many good and useful things. And so we may say the soul grows.

R. But we do not give the soul food, mother, to make it grow, as we do the body.

M. No, my son. We cannot feed the soul, as we do a little child, when it is hungry. But we teach the soul a good many things. And this *teaching is the food of the soul.*

R. Mother, I wish you would teach me a great many things, so that my soul may grow fast, and be as large as uncle John's.

M. That I shall be glad to do, my son, and I hope you will make as good a man as your uncle John, too. But tell me, Robert, is your soul any thing like a pebble, a rose, or a watch?

R. No, mother, but *my body is;* because my body has weight, hardness, form, colour, and parts; and so has a pebble, a rose, and a watch.

M. How many things can you see, Robert?

R. Mother, I cannot tell you how many things I can see. I can see almost every thing.

M. Can you see my soul, Robert?

R. No, mother, and you cannot see mine. I cannot see my own soul; but I can think how it thinks.

M. When you see things, what do you see?

R. I see how they look, mother. I see whether they are round or square; or long or short; or large or small; or red, or white, or black, or green, or yellow.

M. Then you see their form and their colour.

R. Yes, mother, and I can see how far off they are.

M. You can hear a great many different things, making a great many different kinds of sound.

R. Yes, mother, I can hear the bell when it rings for church; and the stage-horn when the driver blows it; and the flute when uncle John plays on it; and the chickens, and the ducks, and the cow, and the sheep, and Eliza when she cries. Oh! how many things I can hear!

M. Can you hear my soul, Robert?

R. I can hear *you,* when you speak, mother.

M. Yes, I think what I am going to say to you, and then, I think to have my tongue and my lips move; and I speak, and you hear the sound of my voice. Put your ear to this watch. Do you hear anything?

R. Yes, mother, it goes, tick-tick, tick-tick.

M. Now put your ear close to my head. I am going to think. Try, if you can hear my thinking.

R. No, mother, I cannot at all.

M. My soul, then, makes no noise when it is thinking, and you cannot hear my soul, you can only hear my voice when I tell you what I am thinking.

R. That is very strange, mother. The soul must be very different from any thing that I can see or hear.

M. Yes, my son. And can you taste, or smell, or touch my soul?

R. No, mother; and I cannot taste, or smell, or touch my own soul.

M. You cannot tell, then, whether your soul is round or square, or long or short, or red or white, or black, or green, or yellow. You do not know that is has any form or colour at all. You cannot tell whether your soul sounds like a bell, or like a flute, or like any other thing. You do not know that it has any sound at all. You cannot tell whether your soul tastes like any thing. You do not know that it has any taste at all. You cannot tell whether your soul smells like any thing. You do not know that it has any smell at all. You cannot tell whether your soul is hard or soft, or whether it feels like any thing. You do not know that it can be felt at all.

R. What do you call all those things, mother, that I can see, and hear, and taste, and smell, and touch?

M. We call them *matter;* and we say they are *material.*

R. Then my *body is material.*

M. Yes, my son, but your *soul is not material. Or, what is the same thing, your soul is immaterial.*

R. Mother, I suppose *your soul,* too, is immaterial; for I cannot see it, nor hear it, nor taste it, nor smell it, nor touch it.

M. Yes, every body's soul is immaterial. Remember, my son, that you have a body and a soul. Your body you can see, and hear, and taste, and smell, and touch. It is like the pebble, the rose, and the watch. *It is matter. It is material.* Your soul has not form, or colour, or sound, or taste, or smell, or hardness, or softness. *It is not matter. It is immaterial;* or, what is the same thing, we call it *spirit.* The rose, the pebble, and the watch have no spirit.

But you look a little sleepy. Go to bed, and to-morrow we will talk again about the soul.

MOTHER HUBBARD

AND

HER DOG:

DERBY:
Printed by and for
THOMAS RICHARDSON, FRIAR-GATE.

Mother Hubbard is merrily laughing
er droll Dog smoking and quaffing!

OLD Mother Hubbard
Went to the cupboard
To give her Doggie a bone;
But when she came there,
The cupboard was bare,
And so the poor Dog got none.

went to the baker's
'o buy him some bread;
when she came back
he poor Dog was—dead!

She went to the undertaker's
To get him a coffin;
And when she came back
The Dog was—laughing.

She went to the market
To buy him some tripe;
And when she came back
He was smoking his pipe.

went to the alehouse
'o buy him some beer;
l when she came back
Ie sat in the chair.

She went to a tavern
For white wine and red;
And when she came back
He stood on his head.

She went to the fruiterer's
To buy him some fruit;
And when she came back
He was playing the flute

She went to the tailor's
To buy him a coat;
And when she came back
He was riding a goat.

She went to the hatter's
To buy him a hat;
But when she came back
He was feeding the cat.

She went to the barber's
To buy him a wig;
And when she came back
He was dancing a jig.

She went to the shoe-shop
To buy him neat shoes;
But when she came back
He was reading the news

She went to the sempstress
To buy him some linen;
And when she came back
The Dog was spinning.

She went to the hosier's
To buy a pair of hose;
And when she came back
He was drest in his clot

The Dame made a courtesy,
The Dog bow'd very low;
The Dame said, Your Ser-
vant, Sir,
The Dog said, Bow-wow.

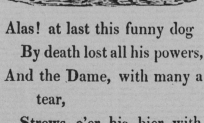

Alas! at last this funny dog
By death lost all his powers,
And the Dame, with many a
tear,
Strews o'er his bier with
flowers.

Finis

THE JUVENILE GAZETTEER.

PRICE ONE PENNY.

A HIGHLANDER.

THE Highlands is the northern district of Scotland, and is formed of an assemblage of vast dreary mountains; not, however, without some fertile valleys on the northern and eastern shores. The cattle in this part of the country are very diminutive.

AN ENGLISHMAN.

ENGLAND is the southern part of Great Britain. The manufactures and commerce of this country are vast, extensive, and various; and her navy is the most formidable in the world. London is the capital, which contains 1,009,546 inhabitants.

A DUTCHMAN.

HOLLAND, or Dutch Netherlands, country of Europe. The inhabits of this nation afford a striking of, that persevering industry is able of conquering every disadvantage of climate and situation; for withstanding all the obstacles ich Nature has placed in their y, they are but little inferior to ir more favoured neighbours. Amdam is the capital.

A CANADIAN INDIAN.

CANADA is a large country of North America. A remarkable earthquake happened here in 1663, which overwhelmed a chain of mountains above 300 miles long, and changed their immense tract into a plain. It is now in the possession of the English. York and Quebec are the chief towns.

A TURK.

TURKEY is a large empire, extending over part of Europe, Asia, and Africa. The Turks are generally robust, well-shaped, and of a good mien. The established religion is Mahometanism; but they are charitable towards strangers, let their religious faith be what it will. Constantinople is the capital of all Turkey, and contains about 520,000 inhabitants.

AN ARABIAN.

ARABIA is a country of Asia. The abitants are of a middle stature brown complexion, and have als a grave and melancholy air. y derive their subsistence from r flocks, from hunting, and from t they acquire by plunder.

A GREEK.

GREECE is the ancient name of that part of Turkey in Europe which contains Macedonia, Albania, Janna, Livadia, the Morea, the Archipelago, and Candia. This unfortunate country has been for some time the seat of oppression and war.

A RUSSIAN.

RUSSIA is a vast empire, partly in Asia and partly in Europe. This empire, exclusive of the acquisitions from the Turks and from Poland, forms a square, whose sides are 2,000 miles each. Petersburgh is the capital of the whole empire, and contains about 300,000 inhabitants.

A SPANIARD.

SPAIN is a kingdom of Europe, 700 miles long, and 500 broad. Anciently it was celebrated for gold and silver mines; but since the discovery of America no attention has been paid to them. The established religion is popery. Madrid is the capital, and contains about 200,000 inhabitants.

AN EAST INDIAN.

EAST Indies is the name given by Europeans to that vast tract of country in Asia, which is situated to the south of Tartary, between Persia and China, as well as to a great number of islands in the Indian Ocean extending from the peninsula of Hindoostan to the east and south.

A NATIVE OF TLASCALA.

TLASCALA is a province of Mexi This country is often visited violent tempests and inundatior Yet this is allowed to be the m populous country in all Americ and it produces so much maize, tl hence it had the name of Tlasca the Land of Bread.

A NATIVE OF MEXICO.

MEXICO, or New Spain, is an extensive country of North America, and is 2,000 miles long, and, in its widest part, above 600 broad. It is celebrated for its mines of gold and silver. Mexico is the capital, which contains above 200,000 inhabitants.

A FRENCHMAN.

FRANCE is an extensive country of Europe, being 625 miles from north to south, and something more from east to west. The industry of the inhabitants, joined to its natural advantages, render it one of the most fertile countries in Europe. Paris is the metropolis, which contains 546,896 souls.

A NEW ZEALANDER.

New Zealand is an island in t Pacific Ocean. The men are sto and fleshy; but none of them a corpulent: they are also exceeding vigorous and active. In some pa of the country the inhabitants are large tribes, and are continually war with each other.

A WELCHMAN.

WALES is a principality in the west of England, 120 miles long, and 80 broad. The country is mountainous, but not barren, producing all the necessaries of life. It is the part of the island to which the ancient Britons fled, when Great Britain was invaded by the Saxons.

A NATIVE OF VIRGINIA.

VIRGINIA is one of the United States of America, and is 446 miles long, and 224 broad. Here are mines of lead, copper, iron, and coal. The principal produce is tobacco, wheat, and maize; but the culture of tobacco has considerably declined in favour of that of wheat. The capital is Richmond.

A CHINESE.

CHINA is an extensive country Asia. It is bounded on the north Tartary, from which it is separa by a stupendous wall. The compl ion of the Chinese is a sort of ta ny, and they have large forehea small eyes, short noses, large e long beards, and black hair. Pe is the capital, and its inhabitants estimated at 2,000,000.

LITTLE·TRUTHS,

FOR THE INSTRUCTION OF

CHILDREN.

VOL. I.

London:

PRINTED AND SOLD BY DARTON AND HARVEY,
GRACECHURCH-STREET.
1802.
Price Sixpence.

THE PONEY.

What a little poney that boy rides !—He has been into the fields with beer for the labourers, he brings home the empty bottles, he carries them their dinner when too far to come for it; he goes to market with a sack of corn and some fowls, and brings home plums from the shop to make

puddings. *Poor little horse; good little boy; if I had that horse I would do so too.*

Yet, I fear, my little Charles would not be long content with so steady a horse as the ploughboy rides; he rode his wooden horse at home so fast as to throw it over, break its head, and make his own nose bleed. *That was not a live horse, and on the flat stones in the yard.* But the same thing might happen on an even road, to those who want to go so very fast, either on a live or wooden horse; live horses have a deal of spirit, and are very strong; some run away with men on them, and what would a little boy do ? *I would hold tight by his mane.* That will not always save a rider; for those who ride with great care are in danger of falling should the horse start. I remember to have read of LAMBERT's LEAP, so named from the providential escape of Cuthbert Lambert, of Newcastle-upon-Tyne, who was riding full speed over Sandiford stone bridge, and endeavouring to turn his horse round suddenly, the beast started and leapt over the battlement; the horse was killed by the fall, it being twenty feet to the bed of the water, but the man was providentially caught in the boughs of an ash, where he hung by his hands, till relieved by some passengers coming that way. I hope, therefore, my children will be careful never to get on a horse without my knowledge.

LITTLE TRUTHS,

FOR THE INSTRUCTION OF

CHILDREN.

VOL. II.

London:

PRINTED AND SOLD BY DARTON AND HARVEY,
GRACECHURCH-STREET.
1802.
Price Sixpence.

IT gives me great pleasure again to meet my children in health; but I am sorry that Charles delights to play with fire; does not he remember to have read, " It is none but a madman will " throw about fire, and tell you it is all but in " sport." I hope he will never play with fire again, for I have heard of more children than one being burnt: I think Hannah remembers what happened to Polly Rust. *Yes: she was one day left alone, and, I think, playing with the fire; her clothes were burnt off her back, and she so scorched as to die the next morning in great pain.* Does Charles hear that? I shall excuse him now; but, when he is found playing with fire again, I shall punish him for it, perhaps more so than by setting him a double task to learn.

I hope Thomas has read his book in my absence: can he repeat the task I set him? Come, speak so as to be heard, and not so fast.

" The hen scratcheth for her chickens with care, when she findeth grain, she calleth them

to partake of it; she sheltereth them under her wings, she defendeth them with all her might.

" The pelican of the wilderness laboureth to get her food, she storeth it up, she bringeth it and spreadeth it out before her young.

" Yet greater love than this hath the mother for her children; she carrieth them in her arms, she suckleth them with the milk of her own breast, she laboureth for them by day, she watch-eth over them by night; she covereth their limbs from the cold air and piercing frosts of winter; she shadeth them from the rays of the scorching sun in summer.

" O, little children! what can you do in return for these great favours? All you can do, is but a little, compared with such love and tender regard."

Well said, my little Tom! I am glad he has been so industrious.

Do they use tobacco-pouches in America? Certainly, my dear: it is the native place for tobacco. It was not known in Europe till America was discovered.

tobacco, and his wife as much in snuff, for several years together; now these pence, thus idly spent, amount (without any interest) in thirty years, to the sum of ninety-one pounds and five shillings! a comfortable possession this for a poor family in the decline of life, and which great numbers have snuffed, spit, or smoked away. It was a very good answer of Omai (whom Captain Cook brought to England) when offered a pinch of snuff, he replied nearly to his effect in broken English: " No, no; me be oblige to you: my " nose is not hungry."

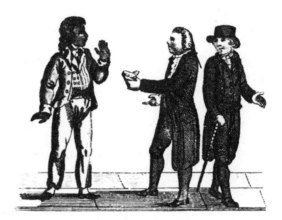

I have been informed, that Sir Walter Raleigh was the first man who smoked it in England. It is supposed he had seen some persons smoke it in his travels, and was desirous of trying its virtues privately in his study. I have read, that whilst he was one day smoking, his servant entered the room with a jug of water (which Sir Walter had called for) who, alarmed at the appearance of smoke coming out of his master's mouth, hastily threw all the water in the jug over him, naturally supposing he was on fire.

Did Sir Walter Raleigh find out the virtues of tobacco? I cannot tell that: neither am I acquainted with all its virtues: but it is, like taking of snuff, become a very idle and expensive custom. I hope no young people, in future, will ever learn to take snuff, or smoke tobacco, without good reasons for so doing. Hundreds of sensible people have fallen into these customs from example; and when they would have left them off, they found it a very great difficulty. Some families unthinkingly spend a moderate estate on this plant.

I have known a man spend a penny per day in

Why do they call some black people Negroes? From Negroland, the name of a large tract of country on the borders of the river Niger, in Africa. *But why are they called slaves?* On account of their being made so by great numbers of people, who go from England, Holland, and France, to several parts on the coast of Africa, and encourage the strong and wicked people to make war, and steal away the inland natives, whom the Europeans purchase by hundreds, and carry into America and the West India islands, where these poor creatures must work as long as they live. Not contented with enslaving the parents, they retain their children's children in slavery. Great numbers of these poor people have no other provision allowed them in many places but what they raise for themselves, and that on the very day of the week set apart for a Sabbath! Great are the hardships they endure on board many of the ships. I have read that six hundred and eighty men, women, and children, were stowed in one ship! which was also loaded with elephants' teeth. " It was a pitiful sight," says the writer, " to behold how these people were stowed. The

151

" men were standing in the hold, fastened one
" to another with stakes, for fear they should
" rise and kill the whites; the women were
" between decks, and the children were in the
" steerage, pressed together like herrings in a
" barrel, which caused an intolerable heat and
" stench." In this situation the poor creatures
frequently die; others attempt to break their
confinement, try to swim back again, and are
often drowned. *I did not think there had been any
people in England so wicked as to do these things.*
Notwithstanding the many humane institutions
in our country, for the relief of the distressed,
and the general love of freedom the people of
our island express, I am sorry to say, that the
lawmakers still countenance the slave-trade,
though they have spoken against it, and condemned the cruelty occasioned by the traffic.
Then what is the cause of its being continued? From
an evil desire of gain; that kind of love for
money, " which is the root of all evil."—To hear
the groans of dying men,—the cries of many
widows and fatherless children,—the bitter
lamentations of a husband when torn from the
arms of his beloved wife,—and the mournful
cries of a mother and her children, when violently
separated, perhaps, never to see each other
again!—I say, one would think, that these
things would so affect the human mind, as to
cause such practices to cease.

*I hope the humane people of England will con-
tinue their endeavours to relieve the distresses of
slavery, and give that liberty to others which they
desire for themselves.*

*When black persons are set at liberty, are they
capable of following trade and manufactures, as the
white people do?* Certainly: I have known good
coopers, carpenters, and printers, who were black
men. The minds of black persons in general are
as capable of improvement as those of the whites.
In England, Ignatius Sancho, a black, wrote
many pleasing letters, which were printed. Phillis
Wheatley, a black girl, of Boston, in America,
wrote some pleasing poems; and many accounts
are preserved in America of virtuous black men
and women.

William Dickson, a native of Scotland, has
written a book on slavery; and, from a journal
kept by a planter's son in Barbadoes, he has given
among other extracts one to the following effect:

" My father, in the year 1760, had a very

" valuable negro, called John. He was master of
" one of our fishing-boats! he understood his
" business thoroughly. He knew the art of
" catching the fish, and selling them to advantage.
" The people in the market had a very high
" opinion of his honesty and skill, and he bore
" the character of being a very fair dealer. My
" father placed unlimited confidence in him, and
" was not deceived. When my father came to
" England, in the year 1761, my mother was
" extremely ill for great part of his absence, and
" John had the government of house, negroes,
" &c. and she thought herself very much obliged
" to him for his great care and attention. He was
" a tolerable scholar; he could read very well.
" He took a deal of pains in teaching me to read.
" He gave me in my infancy good advice; and
" particularly before I was coming to England
" for education, in the year 1761, I have sat with
" him for hours by the sea-side, while he was
" mending his nets, and used to ask him many
" questions about England, about learning, &c.
" &c. He gave me a pretty good notion of the
" manners and customs of England, and of the

152

"things which would be taught me at school; "and used to exhort me very much to be "*submissive to my masters and superiors.* I feel "to this day some impression of the excellent "advice which has been given me by John! "and I have a very great respect for his memory."

After these testimonies of African capacity, can any persons now suppose that the Blacks are not as rational beings as the Whites? I hope the number of those who have represented them as a degraded set of beings in creation are very few. Facts are stubborn things; and however the Blacks may have been degraded, there have been both men and women among them of great capacities, of liberal sentiments, and charitable dispositions. For the present we will drop this discourse.

Hannah, ring the bell for Molly; desire her to bring a cup of chocolate as soon as she can; for it looks so pleasant, I think a walk to Windmill Hill would contribute to health.

What do they grind at the windmill? Wheat; which makes flour, bran, and pollard; and, sometimes, oats to make oatmeal.

Then mills are useful things. Yes; a good invention. Some work by water, some by wind, others are worked by horses, and some are now worked by steam; and are so contrived as to saw wood, hammer out iron and copperplates; some grind tobacco leaves and stalks into snuff; and at Manchester, which is in the North of England, they have a mill for spinning cotton-wool into thread. I am told there is a mill now invented for weaving of cloth; and I have seen one so contrived as to split leather.

I was once informed, that a farmer's man outwitted some Gipsies in the following manner:—Going with an empty cart to London, two

or three women requested they might ride, and they promised to tell him his fortune: " Tell my "fortune? (said the countryman) you do not "know your own!" "—That we do (said one "of them) and we will tell your fortune, only "let us ride." At last he consented, and they "rode quietly for two or three miles, when, by "the way-side, coming to a pond, upon Stamford-Hill, he got upon the copse of the cart, and drove in to water his horses: it was necessary he should unrein the horse in the shafts, and in doing which, he slily slipped out the plugs that kept up the body of the cart; when the horses had

drank sufficiently, he drove them out of the pond, and at the same time shooting the Gipsies into the water, he called out, " You tell my fortune! I told you, you did not know your own, or you would not have got into my cart:" so drove on to London as fast as he could, leaving the Gipsies to walk out of the pond, which was not very deep, but sufficient to give those pretenders to foreknowledge a good ducking.

The History of Jack the Giant Killer

Kind Reader, Jack makes you a bow,
The hero of giants the dread;
Whom king and the princes applaud
For valour, whence tyranny fled.

Jack; who saw the monsters approaching, and put on his cap of knowledge, to consider how he might best extricate himself from portending dangers.

The giant and friend, arm in arm,
　John liked not the looks of Rebecks;
He found a strong cord with a noose,
　And briskly slipt over their necks.

He fastened the cord to a beam,
　And boldly slid down with his sword;
He severed their heads in a trice;
　To free all confined he gave word.

In Cornwall, on Saint Michael's Mount,
　A giant full eighteen feet high,
Nine feet round, in cavern did dwell,
　For food cleared the fields and the sty.

And, glutton, would feast on pour souls,
　Whom chance might have led in his way;
Or gentleman, lady, or child,
　Or what on his hands he could lay.

He went over to the main land, in search of food, when he would throw oxen or cows on his back, and several sheep and pigs, and with them wade to his abode in the cavern.

Till Jack's famed career made him quake,
　Blew his horn, took mattock and spade;
Dug twenty feet deep near his den,
　And covered the pit he had made.

The giant declared he'd devour
　For breakfast who dared to come near;
And leizurely did Blunderbore
　Walk heavily into the snare.

Then Jack with his pickaxe commenced,
　The giant most loudly did roar;
He thus made an end of the first—
　The terrible Giant Blunderbore.

His brother, who heard of Jack's feat,
　Did vow he'd repent of his blows,
From Castle Enchantment, in wood,
　Near which Jack did shortly repose.

This giant, discovering our hero, weary and fast asleep in the wood, carried him to his castle, and locked him up in a large room, the floor of which was covered with the bones of men and women. Soon after, the giant went to invite his friend Rebecks, to make a meal of

History informs us that he took the keys of the castle from the girdle of Giant Blunderbore, and made search through the building; where he found three ladies tied up by the hair of their heads to a beam; they told him their husbands had been killed by the giants, and themselves were condemned to death, because they would not partake of the remains of their deceased husbands. Ladies, said Jack, I have put an end to the wicked monster and his giant friend Rebecks !

Great lords and fine ladies were there,
　Suspended or tied to great hooks;
Most heartily thanked our friend John;
　Recorded his fame in those books.

The ladies all thought him divine,
　The nobles invited him home:
The castle he gave for their use,
　And he for adventures did roam.

At length John came to a handsome building, he was informed was inhabited by an enormous Welchman, the terror of the surrounding neighbourhood, not very likely to prove friendly to our hero, and gave a genteel rat, tat, too, at the door.

At this Giant-castle, most grand,
　The Welchman meets John at the door;
Gives welcome, and food, and a bed,
　But Jack saves his life on the floor.

The old account of this difficult season informs us that John overheard the giant Welchman utter the following not very agreeable lines:—

Though here you lodge with me this night,
You shall not see the morning light;
My club shall dash your brains out quite!

John's considering cap is again in request, and finding a log of wood he placed it between the sheets, and hid himself, to witness the giant's anger and club law.

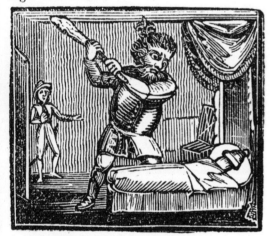

Mid darkness, the giant his bed
　Belabours the post John put there;
And safe in the corner he crept,
　Behind the great giant's arm chair.

Early in the morning Jack walked into the giant's room, to thank him for his lodging. The giant surprised to see him, so early he appeared to say, and continued—

You slept well, my friend, in your bed?
　Did nought in your slumbers assail?
John did to his querist reply,
　A rat gave some flaps with his tail.

Jack thanked the giant for his excellent night's sleep, and although the Welchman was surprised that he had not killed him, he did not express more, but fetched two large bowls of pudding, for his own and his lodger's repast, thinking Jack never could empty one of them.

Hasty pudding for breakfast was brought,
　And John took much more than his friend;
Which slipt in his large leather bag,
　The giant could not comprehend.

Says Jack, Now I'll shew you a trick—
　" A tat " for a giant's trap-door!
He ript up his large leather bag,
　And breakfast bespatter'd the floor.

Ods splutter hur nails, says his host,
　Hur can do that too, without dread;
But Taff made a fatal attack,
　And Jack in a trice doff'd his head.

John seized all his riches and house,
　And bountiful was to the poor;
The pris'ners released from their chains,
　Which bound them in pain to the floor.

In search of new adventures, our hero beheld a relative of the late highlander, dragging to the abode Jack had made his own by stratagem, a noble Knight and his affianced lady, and soon determined his mode of deliverance for them.

A cousin, not heard of his fate,
　Seized Sir Knight and a lady so fair,
When coming to see giant friend,
　And dragg'd them with force by the hair.

Jack donn'd his invisible coat,
　Sharp sword and swift shoes for the fray;
He rescued the knight and the fair,
　And great mighty giant did slay.

His cap for much knowledge and skill,
　He used in encounters most rare;
His sword* all the giants did kill,
　For speed none his shoes could compare.

* This sword was probably presented to him in the armory, of Warwick, Banbury, Broughton, or Northampton Castles; or the Tower.

St. George the great dragon did slay,
   Hunters wild boars make compliant,
And beasts of the forest way-lay;
   Jack is the dread of the giant.

Pray who has not heard of his fame?
   His actions so bold and unpliant;
The friend of the rich and the poor,
   But never afraid of a giant.

A monster had heard of his fame,
   And vowed he would render him pliant;
He sat on a stone at his door,
   Jack cut off the nose of the giant.

Jack having hitherto been successful, determined not to be idle; he therefore resolved to
travel, and to take his horse of matchless speed,
his cap of knowledge, his sword of sharpness,
his elastic shoes of swiftness, and invisible
coat, over hill and dale.

Tradition states, that Jack passed through
the counties of Oxford, Warwick, and Northampton; and visited the University, Crouch-hill,
Banbury-cross and Castle, the Amphitheatre in
Bear-garden, Wroxton, Edge-hill, &c.

He travelled the country round,
   East, west, north and south, far and near;
Abroad or at home he was found,
   Where he of a giant could hear.

Jack was informed by an old hermit, at the
foot of a high mountain, of an enchanted castle,
at the top of the mount inhabited by Galligantus
and a magician, where they had imprisoned a
duke's daughter and her companions: he soon
climbed to the summit, and read these lines:—
   Whoever can this trumpet blow,
   Shall cause the giant's overthrow.

Jack blew a loud shrill blast, having on
his invisible dress, with his trusty sword by
his side: the giant and magician looked for
the intruder, but soon exhibited each an headless
trunk, when he released the inmates, whom he
wished to share the vast riches of the magician's
treasury. The duke's daughter plainly informed
him that she would willingly do so on one condition, which was speedily arranged on the
arrival of the duke and his duchess.

He soon found the edge of his blade,
   Became a most humble suppliant;
And, while he complained of the pain,
   Jack took off the head of the giant.

Jack threatens,—all braggarts beware!
   And coward poltroons he makes pliant;
And thus all vain-glorious puffs
   Are silenced as Jack served the giant.

The Castle-enchantment he razed,
   Magician is made more compliant,
Duke's daughter he rescues from harm,
   Lords, ladies, he saves from the giant.

Duke's daughter, with riches in store,
   To admire our hero not slack;
In marriage they soon did unite,
   The king gave great riches to Jack.

His wife and his children were kind,
   Friends place in him great reliance;
His boys were at college refined,
   His girls told the tale of the giants.

FRONTISPIECE.

The Lion, the Zebra, the Camel, all wait,
Their names and their qualities here to relate;
Whilst a youthful historian sits ready to write,
And the Monkey attends to the scene with delight.

AN
ALPHABETICAL ARRANGEMENT
of ANIMALS *for*
LITTLE NATURALISTS
by
SALLY SKETCH.

From this nice Book I plainly see
You all must learn A. B. C. D.

Published Jan.y 1.st 1821. by
HARRIS & SON,
Corner of St Pauls Church Yard.

A a

is an Ape, as the reader may see,
who gets at the Apples by shaking the Tree.

B b

B is the Beaver, of which you may read
In natural history. wonders indeed.

K   k

K, Kanguroos! _ I see you're not sleeping,
But out of a pocket your young ones are peeping.

M   n

M is the Monkey, a mischeivous elf,
But well he knows how to take care of him

U   u

U is the Urchin; or perhaps if I tell,
His name is a Hedge-Hog, you'll know him as well.

V

V is the Vansire, a Weasel no doul
In the African Islands by some one found

Easy Lessons

Miss Page when she was six years old was too fond of sweet-meats, and such sort of trash, which were not fit for her to eat. Her aunt told her that if she went on so, she would not have a tooth in her head when she was grown up; but Miss Page did not choose to mind what her aunt said, so her first set of teeth soon dropt out, and then came a new set in their stead, which in a short time had holes in them, for she would pick them with pins, and they grew quite black; these teeth did not drop out, for they were fast in the jaw with long fangs. Miss Page would have been glad if they had dropt out, for she had the tooth-ache, which is a bad pain; and she could not eat in the day, or sleep by night, but would lie in bed and cry, " O that I had not eat sweet things to spoil my teeth ! " At last they were so bad that she could not rest till they were drawn one at a time, and two at a time, till she had none left, and then she could not chew her meat, but had it all to mince and sop; and if she got a bit of crust in her mouth, she mumpt and mumpt with her bare gums like an old man; and as for fruit she could not bite it, but eat it with a scoop. Who that has sense and good teeth would eat sweet things to be like Miss Page ?

Miss Ra-chel Bur-ton and Miss Han-nah Cart-wright went to the same school, they had each of them se-ve-ral bad tricks; Miss Ra-chel Bur-ton used to bite her nails to the ve-ry quick, so that it would have shock-ed you to look at her fin-gers, and Miss Han-nah Cart-wright u-sed to sit with her an-kles dou-bled, that you would have thought she had ne-ver learnt to dance in her life. One day Miss Ra-chel Bur-ton had a ring giv-en her, which she put on one of her fin-gers, and thought her-self ve-ry smart in-deed, till a gen-tle-man who saw her with it, said, " Well, Miss Bur-ton, you are real-ly the first per-son I e-ver in my life saw with a ring on their toes." " A ring on their toes, Sir ? " said she. " I do not wear rings on my toes." " Don't you ? " said he. " O no, I see my mis-take, but from the short-ness of your nails, I took your fin-gers for toes." Miss Ra-chel was so vex-ed to think her fol-ly had giv-en cause for this re-proof that she laid by her ring, and left off bit-ing her nails, so in time her fin-gers look-ed a lit-tle bet-ter. But as for Miss Ra-chel Cart-wright, she kept twist-ing her ankles a-bout, till she grew quite a crip-ple, and was not a-ble to walk well as long as she liv-ed.

The Sto-ry I am go-ing to tell is a very sad one. Miss Ju-li-a Sand-ford had a trick worse than a-ny I have told you of, which was, swal-low-ing thread. E-ve-ry end she cut off, in-stead of lay-ing it by, to be thrown a-way, she put it in-to her mouth, and rol-led it up in-to a lit-tle ball, which she let go down her throat, think-ing to her-self, a lit-tle thread is not poi-son, it will do me no harm; but she was mis-ta-ken, it prov-ed to be a dread-ful poi-son, for when it came in-to her sto-mach, it un-rol-led, and got a-bout her bow-els, and ti-ed them to-ge-ther in pla-ces, which gave her such ex-cess-ive pain as you can-not i-ma-gine. Doc-tors were sent for, and me-di-cines were given to her, but all in vain, and so poor Miss Ju-li-a Sand-ford fell in-to fits and di-ed.

FRONTISPIECE.

Death of Little Abel's Mother.

LITTLE ABEL;

OR,

THE YOUNG ORPHAN,

—

AN AFFECTING TALE.

—

WITH THE

STORY OF AMELIA.

LONDON:

Printed for

A. K. NEWMAN & Co. LEADENHALL-STREET.

—

1821.

LITTLE Abel was scarcely turned of eight years old, when he had the misfortune to lose his mother. It afflicted him so much, that nothing could restore him to the gaiety so natural to young children. Mrs. Donaldson, his aunt, was forced to take him to her house, for fear his sadness should still aggravate her brother's inconsolable distress.

They went, however, frequently to see him; and, at last, the time was come for going out of mourning, Abel therefore quitted his; and, though his heart was full of sorrow, he endeavoured to assume a lively countenance. His father was affected at this sensibility: but, alas! it only occasioned him more sorrow, by causing him to reflect that he had for ever lost the mother of this amiable child; and this reflection, every one remarked, was bringing him with sorrow to the grave.

It was a fortnight now, since Abel had been to see him as usual. His aunt always urged some pretext or other during that time, as often as he wished to go. The truth was, Mr. Donaldson was dangerously ill. He durst not ask to see his child, from apprehension that the sight of his condition might too much affect him. These paternal struggles, joined with the former depression of his spirits, so exhausted him, that very soon there was no hope remaining of his cure. He died, in fact, upon the day before his birthday.

On the morrow, Abel, having waked betimes,

tormented Mrs. Donaldson so much for leave to go and wish his father joy, that she at last consented; but he saw that his mourning was now to go on again.

" And why this ugly black," said he, " to-day, when we are going to papa ?—Who is dead now, aunt ? "

His aunt was so afflicted, that she could not speak a word.

" Well then," said Abel, " if you will not tell me, I will inquire of my papa."

At this she could no longer refrain from weeping, but burst out into a flood of tears, and said, " It is he, it is he himself that is dead."

" What, my papa dead ! " answered he: " O Heaven ! take pity on me. My mamma first dead ! what will become of me ? ·O my papa ! mamma ! "

These words were scarcely uttered, when he fell into a swoon; nor could his aunt, without much difficulty, bring him to himself again.

" Poor child ! " said she, " do not be thus afflicted. Your parents are still living."

ABEL. Yes; but where ?

MRS. DONALDSON. In Heaven, with God. They are both happy in that place; and will at all times have an eye upon their child. If you are prudent, diligent, and upright, they will pray that God may bless you; and God certainly will bless you. This was the last prayer that your father uttered yesterday, when dying.

ABEL. Yesterday ! when I was thinking of the pleasure that I should have in seeing him this morning.—Yesterday ! Then he is not buried yet ? O aunt, pray let me see him ! He would not send for me, fearing to afflict me; and perhaps I, on the contrary, should have afflicted him. But

now, as I cannot possibly give him any pain, I would once more behold him, for the last, last time ! Pray let me go and see him, my dear aunt !

MRS. D. Well then, we will go together, if you promise to be calm. You see my tears, and how much I am grieved for having lost my brother. He was always doing me some good or other: I was poor, and had no maintenance but what his bounty gave me: notwithstanding which, I yield myself, you see, to Providence that watches over us. Be calm, then, my dear child !

ABEL. Yes, yes ! I must indeed be calm. But pray, aunt, carry me to my papa, that I may see at least his coffin.

Mrs. Donaldson then took him by the hand, and instantly went out: the day was very dark and even foggy. Abel wept as he went on.

When they were come before the house the mutes were at the door, and Mr. Donaldson's late friends and neighbours were standing round his coffin. They wept bitterly, and praised the integrity of the deceased. Little Abel rushed into the house, and threw himself upon the coffin. For some time he could not speak a word; but at last raised his head a little, crying out, " See how your little Abel weeps for having lost you ! · When mamma died, you consoled me, and yet wept yourself; but now who will console me for your loss ? Oh ! my papa ! my good papa ! "

He could utter no more: his sorrow almost strangled him. His mouth was open, and his tongue seemed motionless. His eyes, at one time fixed, and at another rolling in their sockets, had no tears to shed. His aunt had need of all her strength to pluck him from the coffin. She

happiness of making her quite easy for the remainder of her days. But never did his father's birthday come about, but he was seized in some sort with a fever, on recalling to his memory what he once had suffered at that season; and to those sensations which then affected him, did he impute the principles of honour and integrity that he ever afterwards cultivated during the whole of a long life.

conducted him to a neighbour's house, begging her to keep him till his father's burial was over; for she durst not think of carrying him to see it.

Very soon the bell was set a tolling. Abel heard it; and the woman to whose care he had been trusted, having quitted the apartment for a moment, he availed himself the opportunity, got out, and ran that instant to the churchyard, whither the funeral was gone. The minister had finished, and the grave was filling up;—when all at once a cry was heard of, *Bury me with my papa!* and Abel jumped into the grave.

The mourners were affected at it: Abel was drawn out all pale and speechless, and in spite of his resistance, carried home.

He was, for upwards of three days, continually fainting; and his aunt could not bring him to be composed, even at intervals, except by speaking to him of his dear papa. At length his first excesses of anguish were allayed: he wept no longer, but was very sorrowful.

A worthy merchant heard of this deplorable affair. He had not been without some knowledge of the father; therefore he repaired to Mrs. Donaldson, that he might see the little orphan. He was very much affected at his sadness, took him home, and was a father to him. Abel soon considered himself as really the merchant's son, and every day gained greater ground in his affection. At the age of twenty, he conducted all the business of his benefactor with so much success, that in reality the merchant thought it his duty to assign him half the profits of it for the future; to which recompense he added his beloved daughter.—Abel hitherto had maintained his aunt out of the little perquisites belonging to him; and, by this event, he had the further

OLD FRIENDS
IN A NEW DRESS;
OR,
FAMILIAR FABLES
IN VERSE.

The Boy and the Frogs.

THE task was o'er, thrown by the book,
The careless School-boy sought the brook,
　To pass the time away;
Some young and harmless Frogs were found,
(Abundant upon marshy ground)
　And round the margin lay.

162

With showers of pebbles, stones, and sticks,
The Boy began his wanton tricks,
    To make them dive and swim;
So long as *he* was entertain'd,
It matter not if *they* were pain'd,
    'Twas all alike to him.

A Frog, escap'd beyond his reach,
To aid his brethren made a speech,
    And thus the Lad addrest:
" O, thoughtless Boy, to use us so !
Let calm reflection gently glow
    Within thy youthful breast.

" O think how easy 'tis to find
Diversion to relieve the mind,
    In innocent employ;
No longer then this sport pursue,
'Tis *death* to us, though *sport* to you,
    Unthinking, cruel Boy ! "

The Boy with due remorse was mov'd,
He felt he justly was reprov'd
    For his inhuman whim;
He vow'd no more to merit blame,
But so to act, that just the same
    Mankind might act by him.

The Dog and the Shadow.

A HUNGRY dog some meat had seized,
And, with the ample booty pleased,
    His neighbour dogs forsook;

In fear for his delightful prize,
He look'd around with eager eyes,
    And ran to cross the brook.

To cross the brook, a single plank
Was simply laid from bank to bank;
    And, as he past alone,
He saw his shadow at his feet,
Which seem'd another dog, with meat
    Much better than his own.

Ah, ha ! thought he, as no one spies,
If I could make this piece my prize,
    I should be double winner:
So made a snatch; when, sad to tell !
His own piece in the water fell,
    And thus he lost his dinner.

The fable which above you see,
To greedy folks must useful be,
    And suits those to a tittle,
Who long for what they can't obtain;
'Tis sure far wiser to remain
    Contented with a little.

The Jewel on the Dunghill.

A CAREFUL Hen had hatch'd her brood,
    And led them to the field;
In view a spacious Dunghill stood,
And promis'd store of strength'ning food
    To her young tribe to yield.

With tender care, the anxious Hen
    Around her call'd her young;
She scratch'd, and look'd, and scratch'd again,
But, ah ! not one poor single grain
    From all her labour sprung.

While with unwearied love she tried,
  A sparkling Jewel shone;
With wonder all the treasure spied,
A bracelet clasp! young Fanny's pride,
  By careless Betty thrown.

The Hen, she peck'd, but peck'd in vain,
  Though much it pleas'd her eyes;
The young ones peck'd, and peck'd again,
But, ah! of corn a single grain
  Had been a better prize.

The careful Hen, at length quite pleas'd,
  An apple's core discern'd;
Her infant train the treasure seiz'd,
When each its hunger soon appeas'd,
  The paltry jewel spurn'd.

Though brilliant Gold and Jewels seem,
  They shrink from virtue's test;
Those mental stores good friends esteem
Try to obtain, and always deem
  Whate'er is useful—best.

The Lion and the Mouse.

WITHIN a thicket's calm retreat
  A fine majestic Lion lay;
Glad to forget, in slumber sweet,
  The toils of the foregoing day.

A Mouse too near him chanc'd to creep,
  It knew no fear, nor danger saw;
The Lion, starting from his sleep,
  On the intruder laid his paw.

Imprison'd, and detain'd so tight,
  And so uncomfortably press'd;
The Mouse was in a dreadful fright,
  And thus the royal brute address'd:

" Ah! let me not, Sir, plead in vain,
  Hear me, dread monarch of the wood!
And generously forbear to stain
  Thy paws with such ignoble blood."

The Lion saw its humble size;
  And melted by the strain of woe,
In pity to its plaintive cries,
  He let the little trembler go.

It chanc'd upon a sultry day,
  When scarce a timid beast was met,
The Lion, roaming for his prey,
  Was taken in the hunter's net.

He foam'd, he roar'd, he lash'd his tail,
  His thundering groans the forest fill;
But, ah! his efforts nought avail,
  The Lion is a pris'ner still.

The grateful Mouse, surpris'd to hear
  The noble creature in distress,
Now proves its gratitude sincere,
  By hasting to afford redress.

" Be patient, Sir," she cried, " fear not,
  While I my humble means will try
To show you I have not forgot
  The day you gave me liberty."

The Mouse began to work at nine,
  And ere the morning clock struck three,
Completely gnaw'd the woven twine,
  And set the royal captive free.

The Lion long in vain had storm'd,
  The Mouse with *patience* had begun;
And *perseverance* soon perform'd
  A work rash haste could ne'er have done.

Two lessons we from hence may learn,
  " The humblest not to disregard; "
And that " a kind and friendly turn
  Will almost always meet reward."

The Ass and the Lap-dog.

Happy and gay
  Was little Tray,
His comrade's fare he envied not;
  Both old and young
  His praises sung,
" The Lap-dog at the farmer's cot."

So free and brisk,
  To jump and frisk
Around his honest master's knees,
  Tray was belov'd,
  For thus he prov'd
His wish as well as means to please.

It came to pass,
  The farmer's ass
Had seen Tray fondled and rewarded;
  Thought he, " Good Sir,
  Why love this cur ?
While I, poor I, go unregarded !

" As day by day
  I'm fed with hay,
'Tis plain you cannot quite despise me;
  I'll copy Tray,
  'Twill be the way
To make you still more highly prize me."

So said, so done,
  The Donkey run,
And pranc'd at once into the kitchen;
  Such pranks he play'd,
  So plung'd and bray'd,
He thought his efforts quite bewitching.

The farmer pleas'd,
  With laughter seiz'd,
Now made the Ass grow ten times bolder;
  He tried to kick,
  His face to lick,
And plac'd his hoof upon his shoulder.

" To copy Tray,"
  He gave a bray,
That nearly stunn'd his worthy master;
  But ah ! just then,
  The farmer's men
Reliev'd him from this strange disaster.

The blows fell thick,
  From either stick,
And the poor Ass reluctant went;
  He rued the day
  He envied Tray,
For life till then had been content.

This fable shows,
  That half the woes
We oft complain of are ideal;
  If vex'd we be
  At Heaven's decree,
We well deserve to find them real.

Both high and low,
  True worth may show
Alike—while each performs his best;
  Then, in that state
  Decreed by fate,
Let ev'ry one contented rest.

And many curious things beside
  The Giants in Guildhall.

The post-boy galloping away,
  With letter-bag you'll find:
The wharf, the ship, the lady gay,
  The beggar, lame and blind.

The boatman plying at his oar,
  The gard'ner and his greens,
The knife-grinder, with many more
  Of London's City Scenes.

Countryman on a Stage Coach.

HERE is Farmer Clodpole, who lives a hundred miles from London, coming to see it at last. They have just reached the top of a hill, and catch a fine view of the city.

"What! is that *Lunnun*, coachey? Well, I'm glad to see it at last; for I, that's only used to jog along a few miles in our cart, don't much fancy this jumbling and jolting. But what a smoke they are in, master coachman; I shall be glad enough to get back again, if I am always to be in such a *puther*. Pray, what's that there great round thing in the midst of the housen?—Oh! St. Paul's: why that beats our parish church all to pieces. Well, drive away, coachey, that I may see all the fine things; and nobody shall laugh at me any more, because I have not seen *Lunnun*."

The Scavenger.

I am glad to see this man, whose business it is to sweep up the mud and dirt from the streets, and collect it in a cart. Surely, no part of London needs this work more than Thames Street and Billingsgate; for, even in a dry season, the narrowness of the streets, and great traffic of men and women, with fish in wet baskets, &c. keep the pavement constantly dirty. When the cart is well laden, he empties it into some waste place in the outside of the town, or delivers it at some wharf by the water-side; and as it proves a very rich manure, he finds it a profitable and useful occupation.

The Bellman.

Well, here is the Bellman and Crier, calling the attention of the people to a description of a child that has been lost. The number of children who have of late been stolen from their homes, has caused great alarm to many parents. It was not far from London Bridge that little Tommy

INTRODUCTION

Come, peep at London's famous town,
  Nor need you travel there;
But view the things of most renown
  Whilst sitting in your chair.

At home, an hundred miles away,
  'Tis easy now to look
At City Scenes, and London gay,
  In this my little book.

Yes, there in quiet you may sit,
  Beside the winter's fire,
And see and hear as much of it,
  As ever you desire.

Or underneath the oak so grey,
  That stands upon the green,
May pass the summer's eve away,
  And view each City Scene.

There's great St. Paul's, so wondrous wide,
  The monument so tall,

The poor little soul,
Unus'd to control,
O'er the threshold just happen'd to stray,
When a sly cunning dame,
Mary Magnay by name,
Entic'd the young truant away.

At a pastry cook's shop
She made a short stop,
And gave him two buns and a tart,
And soon after that,
She bought him a hat
And feather, that made him quite smart.

Then a man they employ
To describe the sweet boy,
Whom they sought with such tender regard !
And soon you might meet
Bills in every street,
Which offer'd five guineas reward !

They did not succeed
To discover the deed,
Tho' much all who heard of it wonder'd,
Till at length they sent down
Large bills to each town,
And rais'd the reward to one hundred !

Dellow was taken away, which caused the parish-officers to advertise a reward of one hundred guineas for his recovery, and the bills were the means of his being discovered at Gosport, in Hampshire. It appeared that this little boy and his sister were enticed away by a decently dressed woman, who sent the girl home, but took the boy. Having no children of her own, she contrived to take him to Gosport, and to present him to her husband, on his return from a long voyage at sea, as his own son. The whole history of the distressing loss and happy recovery of little Thomas Dellow is described in verse.

A sweet chubby fellow,
Nam'd little Tom Dellow,
His mamma to a neighbour did send,
With a caution to stop
At a green-grocer's shop,
While she went to visit a friend.

The office of bellman was first instituted in 1556, for the purpose of going round the ward by night to ring his bell, and to exhort the inhabitants, with a loud voice, to take care of their fires and lights, to help the poor, and pray for the dead. This custom, though once general, is used only at Christmas-time, when a copy of verses is repeated, instead of the admonition used in former days.

A Wharf.

Is a landing place by the side of a river, for the convenience of boats, barges, or ships. At these wharfs many casks of fruit, plums, currants, figs, oranges, and lemons, are brought on shore, to be taken away in carts to grocers, fruiterers, and orange merchants. It is the business of a merchant to bring over these things for our use, and for which we are obliged to him. The West and East India Docks receive now most of the shipping used to and from those countries, and are considered more secure from robberies, than the open wharfs by the sides of the river Thames used to be.

Rag Fair and Old Clothes.

Not far from the Tower is Rosemary Lane, where Rag Fair is daily held. To describe the great variety there sold, would exceed all bounds; we would, however, advise every country customer who visits that place, to take particular care of his pockets, that the money depart not without his consent; and, if he takes change, to see well that the silver be good. A word to the wise is sufficient. But as many dealers in old clothes know that an industrious disposition is worth more than good opportunities without it; and as nothing is to be got by standing still, up old Levi gets early in the morning, and rambles about from street to street, and buys old clothes of those who have got new ones: or sometimes he gets a stock of hats and slippers, and then begins his walk again. So, as he wants his money more than he does his goods, he sells them to those who want the goods more than they want their money. Thus both parties are accommodated. This is the business of a trader; and his customers are as much obliged to him for

before it is fit to swim. What a pity that all this expense and trouble should be wasted in contriving to kill our neighbours and destroy their property; when it might be employed to the advantage of both parties, by promoting a friendly intercourse with each other.

The Sedan Chair.

This mode of riding is now but seldom seen, though formerly it was frequently in use. But now Sedan Chairs are used by the sick and weakly, as well as by the nobility and others, who attend at the levees at court. As for us poor authors, we must adopt the plan of riding when we must, and walking while we can.

The Dancing Bear and Dogs.

I wish the bear had remained in Russia or Poland, rather than, after being brought from his native woods, to be thus tormented; for who can tell what misery he underwent in learning to move at the command of his keeper. And as for the poor dogs, they must be very tired before their day's work is ended. I would rather find

letting them have his things, as he is to them for letting him have their money.

Ship-building.

Now we have a distant view of a man-of-war (which is a great fighting ship) building at Deptford. You may see, by the boats in the front, how large it must be; for the further off any thing is, the smaller it looks; and yet it seems larger at this distance, than the boats which are close by. It is like a large floating house, with convenient apartments, sufficient to accommodate 800 people. Numbers of men have been at work on it for several years; and hundreds of fine oaks, which have been from fifty to a hundred years in growing, have been cut down to build it with: besides all the iron from Sweden, for bolts and nails; and fir-trees from Norway, for planks and masts; and copper from Cornwall, to cover its bottom with, to preserve it from being rotted by the sea-water and from other injuries; and the pitch, tar, paint, glue, and I cannot tell how many other things, which must be used

employment for the men, than give them money for punishing poor animals as they do!

The Fire-engine.

We know of no place better supplied with engines for putting out fire, than London; and though fires are very frequent, they seldom do so much damage as formerly, when houses were built of wood, or without party-walls.

An engine is a very clever contrivance: the pipes convey the water over the tops of the houses; and if an engine arrives in time, it frequently prevents the flames from spreading further.

Drawing Goods in a Truck.

Well done, my good boy! and well done, my good dog! why the dog works as hard as the boy, and seems to do it with quite as much ease.

In drawing that truck, boy, you now feel a part
Of what ev'ry horse feels, when drawing a cart.

Come, my lad, haste away, to make room for a fine coach, full of gay people, coming to the East India House.

The Dustman.

Bring out your dust! the dustman cries,
    Whilst ringing of his bell:
If the wind blows, pray guard your eyes,
    To keep them clear and well.

A very useful set of men are these; they remove the dust and dirt from the houses in the city. It is a very profitable business, for, by sifting and sorting what is taken away, every thing becomes useful. There are frequently found cinders for firing, ashes and breeze for brickmakers: bones and old rags, tin and old iron, are carefully separated from oyster-shells and stones, which have their several purchasers.

My masters, I'm dirty, nor can I be clean;
    My business it would ill become,
With my face and hands clean in the street to be seen,
    While I carry my shovel and broom.

The Watchman.

This man has a comfortable great coat, a lantern, and a rattle, with a large stick to attack thieves. I suppose my readers would think it very wrong of him to sleep, and suffer thieves to do as they please: and so it would. But I hope no one will blame the watchman, and do as bad himself; for I have known some little folks, who have had books and teachers, and good advice also, that have not made use of any of them.

Indeed, sometimes, when their teachers were looking at them, they would appear to be very busy and attentive for a little while; but when no one watched them, they would do as little as a watchman when he takes a nap.

The Link-boy.

The Link-boys are always on the watch, with their large torches, at dark crossings and lanes, to light passengers through them. They deserve the reward of a few halfpence, from those whom they assist.

The Lamplighter.

Perhaps the streets of no city in the world are so well lighted as those of London, there being lamps on each side of the way, but a few yards distant from each other. It is said that a foreign ambassador happening to enter London in the

evening, after the lamps were lighted, was so struck with the brilliancy of the scene, that he imagined the streets had been illuminated expressly in honour of his arrival. What would he have thought, had he passed through the lustre which is shed at present by the gas lights, from so many of our shops, and from the lamps in the streets. The Lamplighters are a useful set of men; and they are liable to many accidents while engaged in their dangerous occupation. In the winter, the foot-pavement is frequently so slippery, that they often fall and are maimed, by the ladder's sliding from under them; or sometimes a careless passenger runs against the ladder and throws them down. But one of their greatest difficulties is a high wind. In October, 1812, a poor man, named Burke, who had been many years in that employment, as he was

lighting the lamps on the east side of Blackfriars' Bridge, was, by a sudden gust of wind, blown into the river, in presence of his son, a child of ten years old, and before assistance could be procured, he sunk to rise no more !

The Milkmaid.

If any of my little readers wish to be as healthy and merry as Betty the milkmaid, they must work hard, and rise early in the morning, instead of lying in bed while every body else is about his business, and idling their time till they go to bed again. Betty is obliged to get up as soon as it is light; and then takes a walk into the fields to fetch her cows. When she has milked their full udders into her clean pails, she sets off again, and carries it from door to door, time enough for her customers to have it for breakfast. As every one knows the business of a milkmaid, I shall say no more about it; but advise those to remember her example, who wish to make themselves happy or useful.

The drowned Boy.

New Milk from the Cow.

Ah, silly lad! he would go out of his depth, though he knew he was not a skilful swimmer, and see what has been the consequence! He was seized with the cramp, when he had been a few minutes in the water, and began to sink directly. His brave companion jumped in after him, at the risk of his own life, and has brought him back, quite senseless, to the boat. How distressed his poor brother looks! and how anxious to see whether there is any life left in him.

There is a society in London, of which Dr. Hawes and Dr. Lettsom were the founders, for the purpose of recommending the best means to be used for recovering drowned persons: it is called the Humane Society. They have houses placed at proper distances by the river-side, where assistance may be had instantly; and every possible means are tried for many hours, before they give any one quite over. Numbers have been restored to life by this benevolent institution, and there is a sermon preached once a year, before the Society, when all who have been brought to life by this means are present: it is a very affecting spectacle.

Let us hope they will take this poor boy to one of these places, and perhaps he may yet be restored to his family.

The Flower-pot Man.

Here comes the old man with his flowers to sell,
  Along the streets merrily going:
Full many a year I've remember'd him well,
  With " *Flowers, a growing, a blowing!* "

Geraniums, in dresses of scarlet and green;
  Thick aloes, that blossom so rarely;
The long creeping cereus, with prickles so keen;
  Or primroses modest and early.

The myrtle dark green, and the jessamine pale,
  Sweet scented and gracefully flowing,
This flower-man carries and offers for sale,
  " *All flourishing, growing, and blowing!* "

That lady and her children, who have gone from Cheapside to Islington, may fancy themselves at a farm in the country; the fields look so green, the fresh air is so reviving, and the warm milk so delightfully sweet. Let us hope they will all receive some benefit from their morning excursion; for a walk, and a draught of new milk, must contribute greatly to the health of children who are confined for the rest of the day in a crowded city. The old gentleman on the bench seems also to have had his draught, and is contemplating the fine shape of the gentle cow.

Covent Garden.

Now we have a view of Covent Garden Market, where plants, fruit, and flowers of every kind, are brought for sale from the country. By four o'clock in a summer's morning, it is completely full of the most rare and beautiful plants that can be grown in England, either in open nurseries, or in the hot-house and green-house: and what with the number of busy people buying and selling; the carts going to and fro, laden with flowers, fruit, and vegetables of all sorts; the beauty and gaiety of the different plants, and the sweetness of their odours, it is altogether a most delightful scene. The Londoners cannot take a country walk whenever they please, and enjoy the green fields and wild hedge-flowers, in the open air; but they may supply themselves here with every kind of beautiful plants, for a garden within doors; and to those who have a little knowledge of botany, it must be not only an entertaining, but even a useful amusement.

The Fire-plug.

The turn-cock, as he is called, has just opened a fire-plug, or rather water-plug; but as its principal use is to supply water to the engines for extinguishing fires, it has acquired the former name, more from custom than propriety. Some boys make rare sport, by putting one foot on the stream, and diverting the course of the water; it is thus driven into the air, and over their companions or passengers.

At first sight it seems impossible for water to run up hill; and yet, by a little ingenuity, this is easily done; for, put water into what you please, and one side or end of it will never be higher than the other. It is by knowing and thinking about this, that clever men have contrived to supply whole cities with water, and even to send it up into the highest rooms of a house. They first of all make a great reservoir, or collection of water, on some neighbouring hill, from which pipes are carried, underground, to all the houses they wish to supply; the water in that end of the pipes next the town, always rising as high as that in the reservoir at the other end of them. If they cannot find a convenient spring, sufficiently high, they force the water to a proper height, by pumps and steam-engines; and by these inventions, do with ease, what the best ancient philosophers might have thought impossible.

When one of the great pipes, which run through the streets of London, happens to burst, the water soon forces up the pavement, and a fountain is produced, as represented in the picture.

The Funeral.

The kind and loving mother of those two children is dead, and going to the grave! It is too late now to be dutiful to her, for she cannot open her eyes to look at you, they are shut for ever: it is too late to do as she bid you, for her lips are closed, and she cannot speak: it is too late to wait upon her now, for she no longer requires your assistance! O, little girl and little boy, if your dear mamma be still alive, be very kind and dutiful to her before this sorrowful day comes; or else it will be too late to do any thing for *her*, but cry very bitterly over her grave.

The Charity Children.

These charity children are coming from church, with two parish beadles before them. Several thousands of poor children are taught to read, work, and write, in the different charity-schools of London, and to do their duty to God and to their neighbours; which will enable them to become respectable in this world, and tend to make them happy in the next.

The Black Man's Lament
or, How to make Sugar

Come, listen to my plaintive ditty,
  Ye tender hearts, and children dear !
And, should it move your souls to pity,
  Oh ! try to *end* the griefs you hear.

1. There is a *beauteous plant*, that grows
  In western India's sultry clime,
Which makes, alas ! the Black man's woes,
  And also makes the White man's crime.

  For know, its tall gold stems contain
    A sweet rich juice, which White men prize ;
  And that they may this *sugar* gain,
    The Negro toils, and bleeds, and *dies*.

  But, Negro slave ! *thyself* shall tell,
    Of past and present wrongs the story ;
  And would all British hearts could feel,
    To *end* those wrongs were *Britain's glory*.

Negro speaks.

2. First to our dear Negro land,
  His ships the cruel White man sends ;
And there contrives, by armed band,
  To tear us from our homes and friends ;

  From parents, brethren's fond embrace ;
    From tender wife, and child to tear ;
  Then in a darksome ship to place,
    Pack'd close, like bales of cotton there.

  Oh ! happy those, who, in that hour,
    Die from their prison's putrid breath !
  Since they escape from White man's pow'r,
    From toils and stripes, and lingering death !

3. For what awaited us on shore,
  Soon as the ship had reach'd the strand,
Unloading its degraded store
  Of freemen, forc'd from Negro land ?

4. See ! eager White men come around,
  To choose and claim us for their slaves ;
And make us envy those who found
  In the dark ship their early graves.

  They bid black men and women stand
    In lines, the drivers in the rear ;
  Poor Negroes hold a *hoe* in hand,
    But they the wicked cart-whip bear.

5. Then we, in gangs, like beasts in droves,
  Swift to the cane-fields driven are ;
There first our toil the weeds removes,
  And next we holes for plants prepare.

6. But woe to all, both old and young,
  Women and men, or strong or weak,
Worn out or fresh, those gangs among,
  That dare the toilsome line to break !

  As holes must all *at once* be made,
    Together we must work or stop ;
  Therefore, the whip our strength must aid,
    And lash us when we pause or drop !

  When we have dug sufficient space,
    The bright-eye top of many a cane,
  Lengthways, we in the trenches place,
    And *then* we trenches dig again.

  We cover next the plants with mould ;
    And e'en, ere fifteen days come round,
  We can the slender sprouts behold,
    Just shooting greenly from the ground.

  The weeds about them clear'd away,
    Then mould again by hand we throw ;
  And, at no very distant day,
    Here Negroes plough, and there they hoe.

8. But when the crops are ripen'd quite,
  'Tis then begin our saddest pains ;
For then we toil both day and night,
  Though fever burns within our veins.

  When 18 months complete their growth,
    Then the tall canes rich juices fill ;
  And we, to bring their liquor forth,
    Convey them to the bruising-mill.

9. That mill, our labour, every hour,
  Must with fresh loads of canes supply,
And if we faint, the cart-whip's power,
  Gives force which *nature's* powers *deny*.

10. Our task is next to catch the juice
  In leaden bed, soon as it flows ;
And instant, lest it spoil for use,
  It into boiling vessels goes.

  Nor one alone : four vessels more
    Receive and clear the sugar-tide.
  Six coolers next receive the store ;
    Long vessels, shallow, wooden, *wide*.

1

4

2

5

3

6

7

8

9

10

11

12

While cooling, it begins to grain,
　Or form in crystals white and clear ;
Then we remove the whole again,
　And to the *curing-house* we bear.

Molasses there is drain'd away ;
　The liquor is through hogsheads pour'd ;
The scum falls through, the crystals stay ;
　The casks are clos'd, and soon on board.

11. The ships to English country go,
　And bear the hardly-gotten treasure.
Oh ! that good Englishmen could know
　How Negroes suffer for their pleasure !

Five months, we, every week, alas !
　Save when we eat, to work are driven :
Six days, three nights ;　then, to each class,
　Just twenty hours of rest are given.

But when the Sabbath-eve comes round,
　That eve which White men sacred keep,
Again we at our toil are found,
　And six days more we work and weep.

" But, Negro slave, some men must toil.
　The English peasant works all day ;
Turns up, and sows, and ploughs the soil.
　Thou wouldst not, sure, have Negroes play ? '

" Ah ! no. But Englishmen can work
　Whene'er they like, and stop for breath ;
No driver dares, like any Turk,
　Flog peasants on almost to death.

" Who dares an English peasant flog,
　Or buy, or sell, or steal away ?
Who sheds his blood ? treats him like dog,
　Or fetters him like beasts of prey ?

" He has a cottage, he a wife ;
　If child he has, that child is free,
I am depriv'd of married life,
　And my poor child were *slave* like *me*.

" Unlike his home, ours is a shed
　Or pine-tree trunks, unsquar'd, ill-clos'd ;
Blanket we have, but not a bed,
　Whene'er to short, chill sleep dispos'd.

" Our clothing's ragged. All our food
　Is rice, dried fish, and Indian meal.
Hard, scanty fare ! Oh, would I could
　Make White men Negroes' miseries feel ! "

" But could you not, your huts around,
　Raise plants for food, and poultry rear ?
You might, if willing, till your ground,
　And then some wants would disappear."

" Work for ourselves and others, too ?
　When all our master's work is o'er ;
How could we bear our own to do ?
　Poor, weary slaves, hot scourg'd, and sore !

" Sometimes, 'tis true, when Sabbath-bell
　Calls White men to the house of pray'r,
And makes poor blacks more sadly feel
　'Tis though *slaves* have no *business* there :

" Then Negroes try the earth to till,
　And raise their food on Sabbath-day ;
But Envy's pangs poor Negroes fill,
　That we must *work* while others *pray*.

" Then, where have we *one* legal right ?
　White man may bind, whip, torture slave.
But oh, if we but strike one White,
　Who can poor Negro help or save ?

" There are, I'm told, upon some isles,
　Masters who gentle deign to be ;
And there, perhaps, the Negro *smiles*
　But *smiling* Negroes *few* can see.

" Well, I must learn to bear my pain ;
　And lately, I am grown more calm ;
For Christian men come o'er the main,
　To pour in Negro souls a balm.

" They tell us there is one above
　Who died to save both bond and free ;
And who, with eyes of equal love,
　Beholds White man, and *humble me*.

" They tell me if, with patient heart,
　I bear my wrongs from day to day,
I shall, at death, to realms depart,
　Where God wipes every tear away !

" Yet still, at times, with fear I shrink ;
　For when with sense of injury prest,
I burn with rage ! and *then* I think
　I ne'er can *gain* that place of rest."

12. He ceas'd ; for here his tears would flow,
　And ne'er resum'd his tale of *ruth*.
Alas ! it rends my heart to know
　He only told a *tale of truth*.

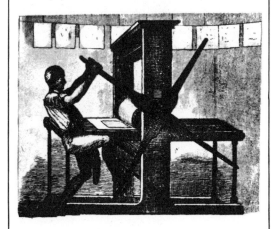

LITTLE
JACK OF ALL TRADES,

WITH

SUITABLE REPRESENTATIONS.

PART I.

LONDON:
PRINTED AND SOLD BY DARTON AND HARVEY,
GRACECHURCH-STREET.
1806.

ADDRESS

FROM THE

PRINTER TO HIS LITTLE READERS.

CHILDREN, for this small book some thanks are due,
The Printer made it purposely for you:
Each trade, that with advantage can employ,
The active man and the ingenious boy,
Is here describ'd, in diction smooth and plain;
If you're improv'd his toils are not in vain:
Yet, to illustrate clear the flowing text,
Behold the picture to each trade annext.
The Printer's labours give the living bread,
And with a living fame he crowns the dead:
'Tis he records the laws of ev'ry art,
And science sends to the remotest part.
His letters, twenty-six, to us have brought,
Sublimest wonders of the human thought !
But in one valu'd book his labours shine.—
Honour'd that art which speaks of things divine.

A PERUSAL of this work will convince my little readers, that industry is the source of private happiness and public grandeur; for to it families owe their support, and nations the advantages of commerce.

Commerce unites men of all countries, and scatters plenty and variety over the earth, by diffusing those productions which would otherwise be confined to their native soil. Society resembles a bee-hive, where, in producing a store of sweets, all are employed—all live cheerfully—and whilst each individual works for the general good, the whole community works for him. The baker supplies the bricklayer, the gardener, and the tailor, with bread; and they, in return, provide him with shelter, food, and raiment: thus, though each person is dependent on the other, all are independent.

How grateful should youth feel, when put by their parents or friends, to honest men and useful trades: they then become members of society, and are thus not only enabled to maintain themselves and future families, but are placed in the way to gain the esteem and respect of the world; for honour always attends a diligent application to our calling in life, whatever that may be. I, my little readers, when working at my press, am conscious of the utility I am to mankind, and often reflect with pride, that *Guy's noble Hospital* was founded by a BOOKSELLER; and that the great and immortal *Dr. Franklin* was once, like me, A JOURNEYMAN PRINTER.

THE BASKET-MAKER.

BASKET-MAKING is a very ingenious and useful trade. The baker, the butcher, the fruiterer, the fishman, and many others, are indebted to the Basket-maker for the convenient work of his

178

THE BOOKBINDER.

THE loose sheets, printed to make a book, are first folded, either in *two* for *folio*, *four* for *quarto*, *eight* for *octavo*, &c. and then, with a heavy hammer, beaten on a stone, to make them smooth. Being placed in the sewing press, the thread is driven through each sheet, and turned round several pack-threads or cords, called bands. When the backs are glued, the pasteboards are fixed on, after having been cut into shape with a pair of iron shears: a book in this state is said to be in boards. The leaves are either sprinkled,

hands. Millbank, at Westminster, and several small islands in the river Thames, yield a great supply of osiers; the twigs, when peeled, are worked into a variety of shapes, according to what they are designed to hold.

At the school for educating the blind, in St. George's Fields, many of the youths are taught to make baskets. How much more creditable is this than begging; and if blind children can earn their livelihood by following useful trades, those who enjoy the blessings of sight should indeed be ashamed to waste their days in idleness, and consequent poverty.

THE TINMAN.

ROAMING for his meat and drink,
　See the merry tinker trudge it;
With his hammer hear him clink,
　On his shoulders see his budget.

Of my work he's but the mender,
　I'm a Tinman, and make new pans,
Slice, cheese-toaster, meat-screen, fender,
　Nutmeg-graters, kettles, stew-pans.

marbled, blacked, or gilded; if the latter, gold leaf is laid on with size, and dried before the fire, being well burnished to make it bright. The cover, of sheep or calf-skin, or different coloured Morocco, is then pasted on, and the back is lettered, and ornamented with brass tools of various devices, after the back has been prepared with leaf gold; and the whole is then pressed and polished with a hot iron.

Children, particularly, should never suffer themselves to be tempted by the rich outside of a book: often a worthless production shines in gold, whilst many a moral and useful work appears in a plain and simple cover.

THE SHOEMAKER.

LEATHER, after it has been prepared by the tanner and the currier, is made into shoes, boots, and slippers. Among articles of dress, shoes stand foremost, on account of the comfort and security they afford us. Were we to go barefoot, we should not only be liable to catch cold, but our naked feet, exposed to the pavement stones

and gravel, would be cut, bruised, and blistered; or were we in the country, they might be stung with nettles, pierced with thorns, and bit by venomous reptiles, from all which will the use of shoes preserve us.

The pernicious custom of wearing whalebone stays has been long set aside, and it is to be regretted another, equally hurtful and absurd, is not also abolished. Some persons, but more particularly young females, are led away by a foolish vanity of wishing to make their feet appear small, and for this purpose force them into tight shoes. Cramps and corns are generally the consequence; for we hear most aged people complain of pains in their feet, owing to having, when young, worn shoes that were not large enough.

THE TALLOW-CHANDLER.

Our world's a ball, this causes day and night:
At the same time, both sides can't have the light.
Whilst to the radiant sun the one side turns,
To light that left in shade my candle burns.

Dark is dull ignorance—read child, you'll find,
That knowledge is the taper of the mind;
Genius, a sun-beam not within our call,
Whilst knowledge is attainable by all.

THE GARDENER.

When children are good I have currants and
    cherries,
For pies and for tarts I have plums and goose-
    berries;
That boy to a poor man who out his hand reaches,
Shall have my fine apples, my nect'rines, and
    peaches;
Shall walk in my garden, there see them all
    growing,

And learn to improve by my pruning and sowing.
As weeds I hoe up from my bed and my border,
He'll root from his mind each rank cause of
    disorder;
Thank God for those gifts which thus daily he
    showers,
And strive to deserve his sweet fruits and fair
    flowers.

This calling is not only the most ancient, but, in point of general utility, is of the first importance. How wonderful to think that a single bean or pea, placed in the ground, shall produce some ten, some sixty, and some an hundred fold! and how excellent the art to which we owe vegetables, fruits, and flowers.

THE HATTER.

The head's the court of knowledge, reason, wit,
There, in the brain, those noble judges sit;
They rule our actions, and, as they command,
We hear, see, feel, taste, smell, move leg or hand.

180

difference between the former and present fashion of dressing the hair, their custom being much decreased since simplicity has been so universally adopted.

A neat and plain head dress is becoming to all ages; but children need no decoration whatsoever, the most graceful ornament being their own natural hair. Great care should be taken of this; for there is no sight more pleasing than a little boy or girl with hair well combed, smoothed, and brushed; especially when united to a clean face, smiling with kindness and good humour.

The head is wisdom's house, the hat's the roof,
Which I keep tight, both wind and water proof.
I leave the fur of rabbit, hare, or cat,
If beaver's down I get to form the hat.

THE BARBER.

His pole with pewter basons hung,
Black rotten teeth in order strung,
Rang'd cups, that in the window stood,
Lin'd with red rags to look like blood,
Did well his threefold trade explain,
Who shav'd, drew teeth, and breath'd a vein.

A BARBER was formerly a person of much greater importance than he is in these days. A hundred years ago, every barber was also a surgeon and a dentist; he was skilful in bleeding and dressing wounds, and no one was more dexterous at drawing teeth.

They are, in general, a cheerful set of people, rather talkative, and well acquainted with the news of the day, which renders them agreeable to their customers: but it is said they feel a great

PART II

AN AUCTIONEER.

A GOING! a going! for nothing 'tis going.—
My lord, in fine pictures you us'd to be knowing.
Nine guineas? that's something—My lady, once, twice;
My hammer is up, and don't let me say thrice.
To go for ten pounds, such a picture, a sin is!
Eleven? I thank you—pray let them be guineas.
A landscape of Lutherbourg's, great in renown!
Thrice gone! there, I knock the great Lutherbourg down.

THE GROCER.

My shop is well stock'd, neat, convenient, and handy;
Figs, almonds, and raisins, and sweet sugar candy;
Prunes, currants, moist sugar, and treacle, and spice,
Fine teas, barley sugar, and comfits, and rice.

181

With nice Spanish liquorice, when you've a cold;
And coffee and chocolate by me are sold.
If children are good, like good children I treat
  them,
And all my good things, O! how sweetly they eat
  them.

A GROCER is a favourite with all classes of people, young and old; his shop being filled with the most delicious productions, from almost every part of the world. The tea tree is a native of China, and resembles a myrtle; the leaves are gathered three times a year, and are dried in the sun and on sheets of metal. We are supplied with figs from Turkey, and with those small currants used in puddings and mince pies, from Zante, an island in the Levant. The best almonds are brought from Turkey; and the finest dried grapes, called raisins, from Portugal. Of spices, cinnamon is much esteemed, and is the inner bark of a tree growing in Ceylon. The nutmeg tree of Banda resembles our peach; the fruit is enclosed within an outer husk, and is again wrapt in a spicy leaf, called mace. Ginger is the root of a plant, which is either baked or candied. Cloves are imported from the Moluccas; pepper from Borneo; and allspice, or pimento, from Jamaica. Coffee grows in Turkey; but previous to being used, the berries are roasted and ground in a mill. Cacao is the nut of an Indian tree of the same name, reduced to powder; and this, made into a paste with other ingredients, is called chocolate. Sugar is extracted from a cane growing in the West Indies: the canes are boiled, and yield a rich syrup, which forms itself into crystals; the dregs being called treacle, or mo-lasses. The sugar is sent to Europe in hogsheads,

to be refined and made into loaves. That which lies uppermost in the cask is reckoned the best, owing to the dregs falling to the bottom. These canes are cultivated by negroes, purchased for this purpose in Africa; the injustice and barbarity of which traffic embitters all their sweetness. The blacks are human beings, possessed of generosity, kindness, and sensibility; the difference of colour may be merely the effect of the violent heat of the sun where they are born. Were a fleet of blacks to appear on the coast of Kent, and purchase the people like cattle, or take them by force to Africa, they would be more excusable than Europeans; for they never read these blessed words, 'Do unto others as you would be done by.'

THE ENGRAVER.

ENGRAVING owes its origin to the hint given by printing, of which it is an imitation. The copper-plate, when polished, is covered with a thin coat of white wax, and on this is laid the drawing, done in black-lead, red chalk, or some other substance unmixed with oil. By being put in the rolling press, the impression is left on the wax, through which the engraver traces the design on the copper, with his needle or dry point; he then heats the plate, and on cleaning away the wax the strokes appear; these he deepens and finishes with a sharp tool, called a graver. The plate is inked over; the ink is then rubbed carefully off, except what remains in the engraved lines; a paper is laid over it; and when it has received the impression, is called a print. Cards, imitating writing, are done in this manner.

The chief purpose of engraving is to give a thousand or more copies of one drawing or painting. Until very lately, children's books were only allowed coarse wooden cuts: but now the copper-plate engraver condescends to work for them also; and, you must allow, the pictures adorning this work are a very pleasing specimen of his art.

A FURRIER.

In the chill regions, bleak with ice and snows,
   T'wards south and northern poles, for ever cold,
Beavers and ermines wrap in furry clothes,
   And in his shaggy gown the surly bear is roll'd.

In the hot east, and milder western clime,
   Where the sun's beams can fertilize and charm,
Altho' 'tis short, yet, through the wintry time,
   Their garments I provide, to keep you warm.

THE BRICKLAYER.

The line and plummet guide the tool,
And keep the trowel under rule.
The firm foundation lay with care,
Nor build thy castles in the air.

CHARCOAL BURNER.

Though my hands and face are black,
   Honest labour's my delight;
With my charcoal on my back
   I can earn the money white.

THE TAMBOUR WORKER.

Nature brings forth her fruits and flow'rs,
   Most beautiful and gay,
And very much surpassing ours;
   But sooner they decay.

Though more for ornament than use
   The art which we practise,
Let industry be our excuse,
   Which thus our wants supplies.

A Pleasing and
Instructive Story

There was once a naughty little girl, who did not care for what her mamma said to her; and one morning, though she had been told not to go into the street by herself, she set off the very first time she saw the door open. She was so silly as to fancy she could take care of herself, and find her way back again as soon as she wished to go home; so she went along, first into one street, and then into another, looking about at all the things that she passed, and never once thinking about home: she never thought how unhappy her mamma would be, when she found that her little girl was gone from home. At last she began to feel tired, and thought she would go home again; but, when she turned round, she could not tell which way to go: she walked about through one street after another, but could not see any house that looked like her mamma's.

After she had been out a long time, she began to feel very hungry; and, when she looked at the shops which had nice cakes at their windows, she wished very much for some of them. She had no money, nor any body with her to buy her some of them. The longer she walked, the farther she was from home; for she had got into places that she had never seen before; and she began to feel very much afraid.

At length, she saw that night was coming on, and that it would very soon be dark. She was besides tired, and cold, and hungry, and she began to cry sadly. She thought what a sad thing it would be to stay in the street all the night, without any bed to sleep on, or any thing to keep her warm: she wished very much that she had not been such a naughty girl, but had minded what her mamma had said to her. She found that the people, who passed her in the street, were not so kind and good as her mamma: they did not seem to care about her, though she cried very loud, and was shivering with cold.

It grew so dark that she could not see the people near her; but a woman closely passing her, saw her, and asked her what was the matter; the little girl told her that she had lost herself, and could not find the way back to her mamma's house. The woman said she would take her to it; and the little girl was very glad: and, after they had walked a long way, they came to a house, but the little girl knew it was not her mamma's. She said " This is not my mamma's house: my mamma's house has steps to go up to the door, and a lamp at the top, which always burns at night." The woman said, " I know very well this is not your mamma's house; it is mine, and you are my little girl now."

The little girl cried very much, and begged to be taken home; but the woman said, " No, you will never see home again, nor your mamma, nor your brothers, nor sisters; for I shall keep you, and I shall beat you if you tell any one this is not your home." The little girl cried more than before; but she did not dare to say a word, for the naughty woman shewed her the large whip, which, she said, she would beat her with, if she spoke. Then, she took off the clothes the little girl had on, and put her on some old shabby ones, and took her into a ship, which was near the house. Very soon after the ship sailed away, and this naughty little girl never saw her kind mamma, or her nice home, any more.

THE HISTORY

OF

SIMPLE SIMON.

Simon cutting his mother's bellows,
to see where the wind lay.

YORK:

Printed by J. Kendrew, Colliergate.

Simple Simon,
Met a Pyeman,
Going to the Fair;
Says Simple Simon,
To the Pyeman,
Let me taste your ware.

Says the Pyeman,
Unto Simon,
First give me a penny,
Says Simple Simon,
To the Pyeman,
I have not got any.

Now Simple Simon,
Went a fishing,
For to catch a whale,
And all the water
He had got,
Was in his mother's pail.

Then Simple Simon,
Went a hunting,
For to catch a hare,
He rode a goat,
About the street,
But could not find one there.

He went to catch,
A dickey bird,
And thought he could not fail,
Because he had got
A little salt,
To put upon his tail.

He went to try,
If cherries ripe
Grew upon a thistle,
He pricked his
Finger very much
Which made poor Simon whistle.

Once Simon made
A great snow ball,
And brought it in to roast,
He laid it down
Before the fire,
And soon the ball was lost.

He went for
To eat honey,
Out of the mustard pot,
He bit his tongue,
Until he cried
That was all the good he got.

He went to ride
A spotted cow,
That had got a little calf,
She threw him down
Upon the ground,
And made the people laugh.

He went to take
A bird's nest,
Was built upon a bough,
The branch gave way,
Down Simon fell,
Into a dirty slough.

He went to shoot
A wild duck,
But the wild duck flew away,
Says Simon I cant
Hit him,
Because he would not stay

Simon was sent
To market,
To buy a joint of meat,
He tied it to
His horses tail,
To keep it clean and sweet.

He went to slide
Upon the ice,
Before the ice would bear,
Then he plunged in
Above the knees,
Which made poor Simon stare.

He wash'd himself
With blacking ball,
Because he had no soap,
And then said to
His mother,
I'm a beauty now I hope.

He went for water
In a sieve,
But soon it all run through,
And now poor
Simple Simon,
Bids you all adieu.

Printed and Sold by J. Kendrew, Colliergate.

RIDDLE

HOW many hundreds for my sake
     have died !
What frauds and villanies have not
     been tri'd ?
And all the grandeur which my race
     adorns
Is like the Rose beset around with
     thorns ;

Wine and Cakes.

Wine and cakes for gentlemen,

     Hay and corn for horses,

A cup of ale for good old wives

     And kisses for young lasses.

THE
LIFE OF
JACK SPRAT,
HIS WIFE,
AND HIS CAT.

This one ear'd Cat,
Belongs to Jack Sprat.

YORK:
Printed by J. Kendrew, Colliergate.

JACK SPRAT could eat no fat,
His wife could eat no lean,
And so between them both,
They lick'd the platter clean;
Jack eat all the lean,
Joan eat all the fat,
The bone they pick'd it clean,
Then gave it to the cat.

When Jack Sprat was young,
He dressed very smart,
He courted Joan Cole,
And he gained her heart;
In his fine leather doublet,
And old greasy hat,
O what a smart fellow
Was little Jack Sprat.

Joan Cole had a hole.
In her petticoat,
Jack Sprat, to get a patch
Gave her a groat;
The groat bought a patch,
Which stopp'd Joan's hole,
thank you, Jack Sprat,
Says little Joan Cole.

Jack Sprat was the bridegroom,
Joan Cole was the bride,
Jack said, from the church
His Joan home should ride;
But no coach could take her,
The lane was so narrow,
Said Jack, then I'll take her
Home in a wheel-barrow.

Jack Sprat was wheeling
His wife by a ditch,
The barrow turn'd over,
And in she did pitch;
Says Jack, she'll be drown'd,
But Joan did reply,
I don't think I shall,
For the ditch is quite dry.

Jack brought home his Joan,
And she sat on a chair,
When in came his cat,
That had got but one ear,
Says Joan, I'm come home puss,
Pray how do you do,
The cat wagg'd her tail,
And said nothing but mew.

Jack Sprat took his gun,
And went to the brook,
He shot at the drake,
But he kill'd a duck,
He brought it to Joan,
Who a fire did make,
To roast the fat duck,
While Jack went for the drake.

The drake was a swimming,
With his curley tail,
Jack Sprat came to shoot him,
But happen'd to fail;
He let off his gun,
But missing his mark,
The drake flew away,
Crying, quack, quack quack.

Jack Sprat, to live pretty,
    Now bought him a pig,
It was not very little,
    It was not very big,
It was not very lean,
    It was not very fat,
It will serve for a grunter,
    For little Jack Sprat.

Then Joan went to market,
    To buy her some fowls,
She bought a jackdaw
    And a couple of owls ;
The owls they were white,
    The jackdaw was black,
They'll make a rare breed,
    Says little Joan Sprat.

Jack Sprat bought a cow,
    His Joan for to please,
For Joan she could make
    Both butter and cheese,
Or pancakes, or puddings,
    Without any fat,
A notable housewife
    Was little Joan Sprat.

Joan Sprat went to brewing
    A barrel of ale,
She put in some hops
    That it might not turn stale,
But as for the malt,
    She forgot to put that,
This is sober liquor,
    Says little Jack Sprat.

Jack Sprat went to market,
    And bought him a mare,
She was lame of three legs,
    And as blind as a bat,
Her ribs they were bare,
    For the mare had no fat,
She looks like a racer,
    Says little Jack Sprat.

Jack and Joan went abroad,
    Puss took care of the house
She caught a large rat
    And a very small mouse,
She caught a small mouse
    And a very large rat,
You are an excellent hunter,
    Says little Jack Sprat.

——

Now I have told you the story
    Of little Jack Sprat,
Of little Joan Cole,
    And the one ear'd cat.
Now Jack has got rich.
    And has plenty of pelf,
If you'd know any more,
    You may tell it yourself.

Drummer and Sot.

——

Drunk or sober, go to bed, Tom,
    Go to bed, Tom,
    Go to bed, Tom,
Drunk or sober, go to bed, Tom.
T'other pot, and t'other pipe
    Then to bed, Tom,
    Then to bed, Tom,
Drunk or sober, then to bed, Tom

Little Man and Maid.

——

They was a little man,
    And he woo'd a little maid,
And he said little maid, will you
        wed, wed,
I've little more to say,
    But will you, yea or nay,
Will you make a little print in my
        bed, bed.

THE
RATIONAL
EXHIBITION

FOR CHILDREN.

London. Printed by Darton and Harvey.
Grace Church Street. 1800.

GOING a short time since to visit a poor aged woman, I was surprised to find one side of her room covered with printed papers and pictures. She told me they were the collection of her children and grandchildren; who, instead of tearing them, had suffered them to be pasted against the wall; that they not only answered the purpose of covering the ragged places in the paper hangings, but afforded an opportunity for the children to read, and employed her frequently in giving them an account of many of the subjects depicted.

From that, and other places, the following collection was made; and without further ceremony, they are introduced to the notice of the juvenile public.

A remarkable Attempt to rob a Dog.

The faithful animal, it seems, is the property of one *Porson*, of Church Street, Bethnal Green; who, working at a factory at Bow, does not return home above once a month, but has for a long time past made a practice of sending his mother half-a-guinea a week by his dog, who always brought the deposit safe in his mouth. Talking lately of the circumstance in a public house, a person was induced to stop the animal one dark night, near his mother's house; when, in making the attempt, he was so much bitten, that it is thought he will lose the use of one of his fingers: and by the interference of one of the neighbours, who knew the dog's errand, he was obliged to relinquish his fraudulent design.

What a good servant this dog was ! and many of his kind have been very useful creatures: without a dog what labour the shepherd would endure ! Well may it be said, " dogs are faithful creatures; " but they sometimes act wrong from mistake; then *their zeal* becomes dangerous. The bear, which was so fond of his master, that he would have prevented a fly from teazing him as he slept, and in endeavouring to strike it off, bruised his master's face, acted with a good intent; but the effect of the remedy was worse than the disease, and it was not well received.

A remarkable instance of the ferocious obstinacy of what is termed the truly-bred bull-dog, was witnessed at Carlisle, on Saturday last:— A horse belonging to a poor man, a porter, at Stanwix, contrived to get freed from the haltar with which he had been fastened, in Castle Street, and had proceeded several yards on its way home, before the owner was apprized of its escape. Immediately on his discovering it, he gave pursuit, and called to the surrounding people to assist him in the recovery of his beast. A bull-dog also taking the alarm, pursued, and soon coming up, seized the poor animal by the upper lip. The horse, affrighted, ran violently along Castle Street, by the Market-place, through Scotch Street, into Rickergate Street, the dog all the time depending from his lip. Here a crowd collecting prevented its further progress, and turned it again up Scotch Street, where it was met by those who had been its pursuers; to elude being caught by whom, and frantic from pain and fear, it ran into the shop of Mr. Porter, ironmonger, and thence into the parlour, where the family were at tea. After overturning the table, but without doing any other injury, the unwelcome visitors were driven back into the shop, when every exertion was made in vain by the owner of the horse, and several other persons, to extricate the suffering animal from the gripe of its merciless tormenter, till one of the company, with a penknife, put a termination to the existence of the savage brute.

THIS is a view of a *barber's-shop*, when every barber was a surgeon. In addition to this, they made wigs.

At Pekin, in China, *Street Barbers* are very numerous; they carry, as it were, their shops at their backs, consisting of a chair, a small stove,

and the implements of their trade. As they travel, they make a loud *snap*, with a pair of large iron tweezers, to announce their approach. As few or none of the natives shave themselves, it is a lucrative employ.

The art of drawing teeth has of late years been greatly improved on, and many persons now practise the *Dentist's* art alone. A pair of black-smith's pincers were formerly used, and then " *Teeth drawn by a touch* " was never thought of, as appears by an old poem.

An old dame to the blacksmith went,
　For her last tooth gave her pain;
Quoth he, " this tooth I soon can draw,
　" And by it some credit gain."

So he the pincers took in hand,
　And pull'd with might and main;
But these slipp'd off, we understand,
　Which much increas'd the pain.

This made the doctor turn about,
　And sigh in doleful dumps;
" If I can't get a whole tooth out,
　" What must I do with stumps ? "

A Letter from a little Boy.

DEAR PARENTS,

I arrived safe at my uncle's yesterday morning, and found the family well; I wish I could say so now; cousin John is very ill; he has had a narrow escape for his life, on which account my uncle and aunt are much indisposed.

Yesterday after dinner we walked to a farm house, near to the side of the River Thames, intending to regale ourselves with some warm milk. We were scarcely got to the farm house, when John proposed to us to go into a little

boat, which was floating by the river bank. Eliza and George refused, saying that their parents had forbidden them. " Pshaw! they'll know nothing of it," said John. " But brother," said George, " we never ought to do any thing our parents should not know." " Very well," said John, " then I may go and take a run into the meadow, for it is no pleasure to me to be here." Away he ran, and as we thought, with no other design than to run into the mead; but, instead of going there, he no sooner saw us enter the farm house, than he went into the boat. About a quarter of an hour after this, we heard one cry

out for help; we ran after the farmer and his son to the place; but what was our surprise, when we saw the boat overturned, and John underneath the water, alternately rising and calling for help, then sinking again. The farmer's son first jumped into the water, and was just in time to take hold of John's coat as he was sinking, but he had not sufficient strength to bring him out of the water; the farmer then plunged in and brought them both out: but John was without sense or motion. Eliza cried most pitiously. As

for me, I was so alarmed, that I could not speak. George, assisted by the farmer's son, carried John into the house.

The neighbours came to give assistance, and two of them used the means recommended by the HUMANE SOCIETY of London, for recovering those apparently dead; having received instructions from Dr. Hawes for that purpose. George endeavoured to compose his sister; and when she had a little recovered from the fright, " I will go back to my parents," said he, " to prevent their being abruptly told of this accident."

I admired these precautions: but I am at a loss to describe the agitations of his parents, when they heard his recital. My aunt fainted; my uncle, after giving her the necessary assistance, came running to his son: in spite of all his firmness, he could not refrain from shedding tears. How well does a kind father love his children! He forgets their faults in a time of danger. After much pains John was brought to himself; he has been punished for his disobedience, for he was at the point of loosing his life; and he has been pained at being the cause of endangering the health of his parents. Children should be obedient. Adieu my dear parents, give my love to all my acquaintance, and believe me, with great affection, &c.

The Escape.

A large mastiff dog, kept by a timber merchant, to guard the yard, was in general chained by day, and loose at night. A boy in the neighbourhood took an ill-natured pleasure in throwing stones at, and by other means vexing the dog, which, as might be expected, took a dislike to the boy, and shewed it by many an angry growl. It happened one day, that the dog was loose and

ranging about the yard, when he saw the boy enter; immediately he attacked him with great fury. The boy now felt the consequence of his ill usage to the dog, and repented that he had given way to so unkind a disposition; but his efforts and repentance seemed to him to be too late: for the enraged animal seized him by the throat, and in all probability had quickly put an end to his life, had not a young woman entered the yard.

This lass, who loved to exercise benevolence to all around her, had been good-natured and kind to the dog, and was of course beloved by him. She ran to help the boy; but finding her strength was not sufficient to draw off the dog by his collar, she thrust her hand into the dog's mouth! The dog, all furious as he was, when he felt the hand of his friend, let go his hold: and by continued exertions, she kept the dog quiet, and the boy escaped.

a considerable distance: one of these terrible eruptions happening, the inhabitants of the town where Pliny was then situated, sought their safety in flight. The aged mother of Pliny was with him, and, more anxious for her safety than for his own, he resolved not to leave her, though she entreated him to flee from those dangers which she imagined it impossible for her to escape, because of her great age and infirmity; but a little delay might expose him also to destruction. Her entreaties were in vain; for her son preferred the chance of dying with his mother, to forsaking her when in distress. At length she yielded to the tenderness of her son, though she was fearful of retarding his flight. The cinders from the burning mountains fell upon them, and the vapours and smoke, which obscured the air, changed the day into the darkness of night, in which the light of flames only served to direct their steps.

This represents the situation of a man in the water, near Bristol.

As the ferry-boat was passing over the river to Bristol hot wells, one of the passengers, an aged man, by some accident fell into the water, nearly in the middle of the stream; but having a basket of live poultry on his arm, he was thereby buoyed up till taken into a fishing smack, after having been carried by the current above a hundred yards from the ferry-boat.

The cries of the distressed, which they heard around them, made the darkness more terrible. But Pliny's care for his mother's life supported his resolution, and made him capable of great efforts: he carried her in his arms, sustaining and comforting her; till, by favour of Providence, they had arrived at a place safe from the dangers of the falling cinders. Thus were the affectionate mother and dutiful son preserved to each other.

The dumb Boy's Presence of Mind.

In the winter of the year 1739, when an intense frost had covered the River Liffey, in Ireland, with such thick ice, that tents were erected upon it, in which trade was carried on, and fires kindled for dressing victuals; many, attracted by the novelty of the sight, crowded

Duty and Love.

Pliny the younger and his family being at a town near to *Mount Vesuvius*, in Italy, which at different periods bursts out into flames, and discharges great quantities of burning cinders to

upon the river, especially to see a ship of war which was frozen in. One of those spectators happening to tread upon a part where the ice had been broke, and which was slightly frozen over again, suddenly went down: as he sunk, he caught hold of the edge of the ice with the fingers of both hands ! Hanging in that precarious situation, shrieks and cries echoed from all sides, but no one of the crowd ventured to go for the man's relief, fearing that the ice would give way near to the edge of the hole, or that the man might not be able to keep the hold, on which his life depended.

A *dumb boy* on board the ship saw his distress, and being favoured with admirable presence of mind, snatched up an oar, and advancing towards the spot, slid it across the hole, both ends resting a considerable way upon the ice; it had a firm hold, and proved the safety of venturing to the assistance of the sufferer, who grasping the oar, was soon helped out of his extremity.

This is an old print, but on a subject worthy the consideration of every person, because the account of the good Samaritan teaches that love,

which every Christian ought to have for the whole human race.

A cat in the country was fond of roving abroad: in one of her evening journies she met with part of a roasted goose in a trap which had been set to catch a fox; no sooner had she begun to eat than off went the spring; down ran the weight, and up went puss; so she hung by the neck till she was dead.

The Fault amended.

A little boy who had discovered a bird's nest in a thicket, felt a mistaken joy at finding such a prize, and hurried away with it: as he walked towards home he met his sister, who upon seeing the nest, remarked to him how curiously it was formed: moss, hair and wool were combined together, and these were lined with feathers, by the industrious and tender parents, (to provide for the warmth and safety of their young), surpassing the art of many little boys, to frame a similar nest. The little boy, realizing what he had done, brought back the bird's nest to the place where he had found it.

Conjugal Affection.

At Haerlem, in Holland, the inhabitants show to strangers visiting that city the ruins of an old castle, which underwent a long siege, at which the assailants were greatly enraged, promising to spare only the women in the place. The wife of the governor requesting permission to bring out as much as she could carry on her back, without being molested, was answered in the affirmative: when, to the surprize of the besiegers, she brought out her husband, and by this stratagem saved his life.

This behaviour was very commendable, and deserving of imitation. History affords us many examples of similar acts of kindness in wives for their husbands. Though many of the fair sex have often deserved commendation, we have heard of some who have misplaced their affections on animals, giving up their time and property for their support, whilst many helpless children and diseased parents were neglected.—The next print represents the situation of a doctor of physic, who was sent for to visit a lady of this description; who, on attempting to sit down, had

nearly killed a cat, which jumped up into the chair at the same time: in going out of the way of puss, a parrot bit his leg, whilst a monkey on the chimney piece pulled off his wig.

Monkeys do better in their native woods, than when kept in houses; and it is to be feared that many servants have been blamed for the mischief done to china and glasses by favourite animals.

Some persons have carried their love of dogs and cats to such an extreme, as to have fowls or rabbits dressed on purpose for them to feed on; whilst the poor wife and children of an absent soldier or sailor have been sent from their door without being relieved.

From Southey's Letters in Spain, &c.

" When I first found myself in a land of strangers, where conversation presented nothing to me but confused sounds, I was frequently tempted to blame the builders of Babel. The very dogs could not understand English; if I said *poor fellow*, the four legged Spaniard growled at me; if I whistled, even that was a foreign language, and I was obliged to address the cat in Spanish; for *Miz* knew not the meaning of *Puss*. I can now converse with cats and dogs; always my favourite companions; for I love the honesty of the one, and the independence of the other.

" Among the many vices of civilized society, there is none that tends more to generate misanthropical feelings, than that of cruelty to animals. In general they are as badly treated in Spain and Portugal, as in England; but the mode of butchering them is less barbarous *.

* The spinal marrow is pierced with a small knife between two of the vertebrae of the neck, and of course the beast falls immediately.

" I will relate to you a circumstance which occurred at Abo, in Finland. You will admire the despotic justice of the magistrate. A dog who had been run over by a carriage, crawled to the door of a tanner in that town; the man's son, a boy of fifteen years of age, first stoned, and then poured a vessel of boiling water on the miserable animal. This act of cruelty was witnessed by one of the magistrates, who thought such barbarity deserved to be publicly noticed. He therefore informed the other magistrates, who all agreed in condemning the boy to this punishment:—he was imprisoned till the following market day, then, in the presence of all the people, he was conducted to the place of execution by an officer of justice, who read to him his sentence: " Inhuman young man ! because you did not assist an animal who implored your assistance by its cries, and who derives being from the same God who gave you life; because you added to the tortures of the agonizing beast, and murdered it, the council of this city have sentenced you to wear on your breast the name you deserve, and to receive fifty stripes." He then hung a black board round his neck, with this inscription; " *A savage and inhuman young man !*" and after giving him twenty-five stripes, he proceeded, " Inhuman young man ! you have now felt a very small degree of the pain with which you tortured a helpless animal in its hour of death ! as you wish for mercy from that God who created all that live, learn humanity for the future." He then executed the remainder of the sentence.

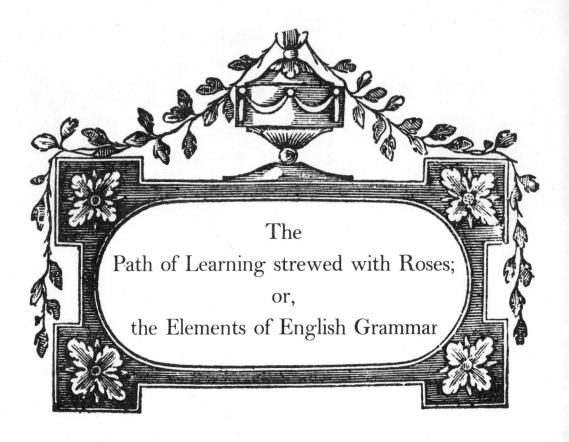

The
Path of Learning strewed with Roses;
or,
the Elements of English Grammar

What parent is there who will not feel infinite joy, when she looks around on her—
  " Smiling offspring; sees by degrees
  The human blossom blow, and every day,
  Soft as it rolls along, shews some new charm."

CONJUNCTION

A CONJUNCTION is used to
join words and sentences together; as—
  "John is going to the park, but I shall not go with him; yet I shall take a walk."
  But and *yet* are conjunctions.

VERB

A VERB is a word that signifies the acting or being of a person, place, or thing.
  Whatever you do is a verb. " I write." " You run." " He jumps." " We walk." " They dance."
  " Emma plays, and Edward listens."—The words *play* and *listen* are verbs.

INTERJECTION

O ! ah ! oh ! alas !
An interjection is a word used to express any sudden emotion of the mind ; as—
  " O dear ! "
  " Alas ! "
  " Ah ! my Pompey ! "

ADVERB

An ADVERB may be added to verbs, to adjectives, and to participles, to qualify their signification ; as—
  " Jane dances gracefully, speaks correctly, and learns diligently."

NOUNS

A NOUN is the name of a thing, place, or person.
  We are surrounded with nouns. Every thing that we can see or touch are nouns.
  Persons—" John, Mary."
  Places—" Garden, Road."
  Things—" Coach, Spade."

The School-Girl in 1820. by W. Upton.

SHEWING THE SAMPLER.

THE colour'd Sampler's work displays
The stitch and mark in various ways,
For ev'ry observer's tongue to praise

THE SCHOOL-GIRL!

GOING TO SCHOOL.

THE darling Child sweet Pledge of Love!
Playful, and innocent as the dove,
With fine new shoes, sets out to prove

THE SCHOOL-GIRL!

THE GENERAL EXAMINATION.

RELATIONS, friends, now that, now this,
Flock round t'give th'heart-glad kiss
And hail with rapturous innate bliss

THE SHOOL-GIRL!

THE SCHOOL.

HOW fast she learns! how neat she sews!
How soon each task she gets and knows!
The watchful Governess proudly shews

THE SCHOOL-GIRL!

NEEDLE WORK.

EMBROID'RY, flowers, and Plain-work too
Th'docile maiden shews to view;
In ev'ry branch a scholar true

THE SCHOOL-GIRL!

TEACHING GEOGRAPHY.

GEOGRAPHY'S instructive Page,
The product of ev'ry clime and age,
Unfolds its volume t'engage

THE SCHOOL-GIRL!

THE DANCING MASTER.

THE graceful Dance next wins the Child,
(Sweet emblem of Affection mild,)
In manners pure, in spirits wild

THE SCHOOL-GIRL!

HOLIDAYS.

THE sportive Holidays, clad in smiles,
That many a care-fraught hour beguiles,
Re welcome home with harmless wiles

THE SCHOOL-GIRL!

THE

COWSLIP;

OR, MORE

CAUTIONARY STORIES IN VERSE,

ADAPTED TO THE

CAPACITIES OF CHILDREN

AT

AN EARLY AGE.

BY THE AUTHOR OF "THE DAISY."

WITH THIRTY ENGRAVINGS.

LONDON:
GRANT AND GRIFFITH, SUCCESSORS TO
JOHN HARRIS, ST. PAUL'S CHURCHYARD;
SIMPKIN, MARSHALL, AND CO.;
J. S. HODSON; AND DARTON AND CO.

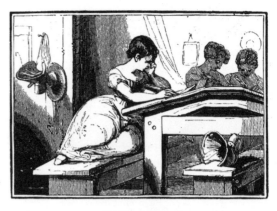

Look at your Copy.

When Frances goes to school, to write,
  I find with great concern,
She never takes the least delight
  To really strive to learn.

Some lines she makes by much too short,
  And some she makes too long;
The copy's seldom where it ought,
  Which makes her write quite wrong.

Such negligence I always see
  With very great concern;
And think what pleasure there would be
  To see her daily learn!

The New Book.

A NEAT little book, full of pictures, was bought
For a good little girl that was glad to be taught.
She read all the tales, and then said to her mother,
I'll lend this new book to my dear little brother.

He shall look at the pictures, and find O and I,
I'm sure he won't tear it, he's such a good boy.
Oh no! brother Henry knows better indeed;
Although he's too young, yet, to spell or to read.

The Crying Child.

O FIE! Master Edward! I feel much surprise,
And am really ashamed of those tears and this
  noise;
Do you know by your crying how sadly you pain
Your mother, although you've no cause to
  complain?
And can you forget, that when sick on her knee,
How she nurs'd you and gave you sweet tamarind
  tea?

A rod is the very best thing to apply.
When children are crying and cannot tell why:
Unless they are babes in the cradle, so young,
That they are not yet able to speak with their
    tongue.

Improper Words.

Who was it that I lately heard,
Repeating an improper word ?
I do not like to tell his name,
Because he is so much to blame.

Go, naughty child ! and hide your face,
I grieve to see you in disgrace !
Go, you have forfeited to–day
All right at trap and ball to play.

At dinner-time there is no place
For boys who merit deep disgrace ;
Such naughty boys I can't permit
With children who are good to sit.

And when at night you go to bed,
The third commandment shall be read ;
For there we find how very wrong
It is to have a faulty tongue.

The Cruel Boy.

Jack Parker was a cruel boy,
For mischief was his sole employ ;
And much it grieved his friends to find
His thoughts so wickedly inclined.

He thought it clever to deceive,
And often ramble without leave ;
And ev'ry animal he met
He dearly loved to plague and fret.

But all such boys, unless they mend,
May come to an unhappy end :
Like Jack, who got a fractured skull,
Whilst bellowing at a furious bull.

The Worm.

As Sally sat upon the ground,
A little crawling worm she found
    Among the garden dirt ;
And when she saw the worm she scream'd,
And ran away and cried, and seem'd
    As if she had been hurt.

Mamma, afraid some serious harm
Made Sally scream, was in alarm,
    And left the parlour then ;
But when the cause she came to learn,
She bade her daughter back return,
    To see the worm again.

The worm they found kept writhing round,
Until it sank beneath the ground ;
    And Sally learned that day,
That worms are very harmless things,
With neither teeth, nor claws, nor stings
    To frighten her away.

The Good Girl.

Miss Lydia Banks, though very young,
Will never do what's rude or wrong:
When spoken to, she always tries
To give the most polite replies.

Observing what at school she's taught,
She turns her toes as children ought;
And when return'd at night from school,
She never lolls on chair or stool.

Some children, when they write, we know,
Their ink about them heedless throw;
But she, though young, has learn'd to think,
That clothes look spoil'd with spots of ink.

Perhaps some little girls may ask,
If Lydia always learns her task;
With pleasure I can answer this,
Because with truth I answer " Yes."

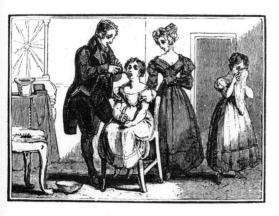

Drawing Teeth.

Miss Lucy Wright, though not so tall,
Was just the age of Sophy Ball:
But I have always understood,
Miss Sophy was not half so good;

For as they both had faded teeth,
Their teacher sent for Doctor Heath;
But Sophy made a dreadful rout,
And would not have hers taken out;
But Lucy Wright endur'd the pain,
Nor did she ever once complain;
Her teeth return'd quite sound and white,
While Sophy's ached both day and night.

Disappointment.

Mamma, shall we visit Miss Hammond to-day ?
As seated at breakfast, exclaimed little Ann:
The morning is fine, and the sun 's very bright,
And I hope you will go, dear Mamma, if you can;
For I 've felt so much pleasure to think of the play
I shall have at her house all the time that we stay,
That I 've scarcely been able to sleep all the night.

So earnest was Ann in her wish to go out,
That when she was silent her looks seem'd to ask,
And to coax her mamma, when she climbed on
    her knee,
And kiss'd her, and promis'd to learn all her task.
They went, and Miss Ann was delighted, no
    doubt,
Till she found Mr. Hammond confined by the
    gout,
And his daughter from home, that she wanted to
    see.

Now homeward returning, Ann said with a sigh,
Mamma, how unlucky our visit to-day;
I expected such pleasure to meet with Annette;
She is always so kind and good-humour'd at play,
And I'm so disappointed, I 'm ready to cry.
Her mamma made a soothing and tender reply.
And taught her to bear what 's in vain to regret.

At Church.

At church last Sunday afternoon
    There was a naughty boy;
        Who talk'd and play'd,
        And noises made,
And would go home too soon,
    And made pretence to cry.

His sister, whom he sadly teas'd,
    Was forced to take him out,
        And kindly said,
        " My dearest Ned,
Papa will be displeased
    To hear of this, no doubt.

" But I will promise not to tell
    This time, if you 'll be good.
        And sit quite still."
        Ned said, " I will; "
And Ned has since behaved as well
    As little children should.

The Dunce.

Miss Bell was almost six years old,
    A shame to tell indeed !
But when the real truth is told,
    She scarce could spell or read.

She went to school and tore her book,
    But never tried to learn,
Sometimes at pictures she would look,
    And turn the leaves, and turn.

Her needles and her thread she lost,
    And often was without;
For though she knew how much they cost,
    She left them all about.

But very much she was disgraced,
    Deservedly, at school;
She wore an ugly mask, while placed
    Upon the dunce's stool.

Susan and Patty.

" Oh ! sister Susan ! come, pray come,
And see how I have cut my thumb,"
    Cried little Patty Green.
" It bleeds ! it bleeds ! what shall I do ?
This knife has cut my finger too;
    How naughty I have been !

" My mother only yesterday,
I know, desired me not to play
    With knives so sharp and keen.
Oh dear ! oh dear ! what shall I do
My father will be angry too:
    I dare not now be seen ! "

Miss Susan said, " I tell you what
We both will do, my dearest Pat.;
    I 'll fetch a little salt,
And tie this piece of riband round;
And when we've covered up the wound,
    Pray tell mamma the fault."

" I think she 'll not be angry much,
If you will promise not to touch
    The things she has forbid."
Miss Patty thought her sister right,
And crept into her mother's sight,
    Expecting to be chid:

But when her mother heard her say,
" Dear mother, do forgive me, pray,
  " I 'll not touch knives again; "
She kiss'd her darling girls, and put
A little plaster on each cut,
  Which soon relieved the pain.

Dancing.

OH DEAR, I must wear my red slippers to-day;
And where are my gloves, and my parasol, pray ?
I'm always delighted when Friday is come,
For I like dancing better than staying at home.
But my mother says dancing was never design'd
To be to positions and stepping confin'd;
But dancing should teach us, in every place,
When standing or walking to do it with grace.

The Hoyden.

MISS AGNES had two or three dolls, and a box
To hold all her bonnets and tippets and frocks;
In a red leather threadcase that snapp'd when it
  shut,
She had needles to sew with, and scissors to cut;
But Agnes lik'd better to play with rude boys,
Than work with her needle, or play with her toys.

Young ladies should always appear neat and clean,
Yet Agnes was seldom dress'd fit to be seen.
I saw her one morning attempting to throw
A very large stone, when it fell on her toe:
The boys who were present, and saw what was
  done,
Set up a loud laugh, and they called it fine fun.
But I took her home, and the doctor soon came,
And Agnes, I fear, will a long time be lame;
And from morning till night she laments very
  much,
That now when she walks she must lean on a
  crutch;
And she told her dear father, a thousand times
  o'er,
That she never will play with rude boys any more.

Quarrelsome Children.

THE currants were ripe, and the gooseberries red,
And very few strawberries left on their bed;
Sweet blossoms and buds were beginning to shoot,
And some were decaying and changing to fruit;
When Charlotte and George in the garden were
  seen,
To walk hand in hand where the gravel was clean.
How pleasing to see them good-humoured and
  merry;
Their cheeks had the bloom of the rose or the
  cherry.
When a butterfly roving, that George chanced
  to see,
Made these happy children at length disagree:
For he, quite delighted, did all in his power,
To catch it when perch'd on a beautiful flower;
And Charlotte, his sister, was angry at that,
And stopp'd little George, and ran off with his hat.
To their mother at last in the parlour they ran,
And noisily speaking together began,

203

The Daisy.

" George shan't catch the butterfly, I 'm sure of
    that."
" I will catch the butterfly: give me my hat ! "
" Such quarrelsome children," the mother replied,
" I find it much better all day to divide;
Go, stand in that corner; and George, do you
    stand
In another; and each hold a rod in your hand."
Though both had been naughty, 'tis proper to say,
They did not their mother's commands disobey;
They went to their corners, and owned before
    long,
For brother and sister to quarrel is wrong.

" PAPA," said Eugene, " is a daisy a book ?
    I thought it was only a flower;
Just now I ran down in the meadow, and look,
    I have found one all wet with a shower.

" A book would be spoil'd, you know, left in the
    rain;
    And could not be read for the dirt;
But a daisy all day in the wet may remain,
    Without in the least being hurt."

" You are right," said Papa, with a smile, " but
    you 'll find
    The Daisy a book, my boy, too,
Containing short tales for the juvenile mind,
    And adapted for children like you:

" And call'd as it is by so humble a name,
    This hint indirectly conveys—
Like the flow'ret it spreads, unambitious of fame,
    Nor intrudes upon critical gaze."

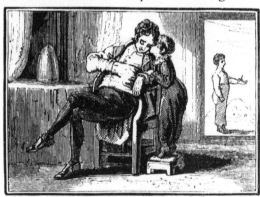

The Sensitive Figure.

" DEAR Uncle ! " whisper'd William Brown,
" Pray will you give me half-a-crown ?
I've seen a very curious toy,
                 I want to buy.

" Charles Mansfield laid it on his hand,
And seemingly, at his command
It mov'd as though his voice were known,
              And tumbled down."
His uncle said, " To gain this prize,
You must first do your exercise:
When that 's correct, you then shall buy
             This curious toy."

The Sash.

MAMMA had ordered Ann, the maid,
    Miss Caroline to wash;
And put on with her clean white frock,
    A handsome muslin sash.

But Caroline began to cry,
　For what you cannot think:
She said, " Oh that's an ugly sash;
　I'll have my pretty pink."

Papa, who in the parlour heard
　Her make the noise and rout,
That instant went to Caroline,
　To whip her, there's no doubt.

The Greedy Boy.

SAMMY SMITH would drink and eat
　From morning unto night;
He filled his mouth so full of meat,
　It was a shameful sight.

Sometimes he gave a book or toy,
　For apple, cake, or plum;
And grudged if any other boy
　Should taste a single crumb.

Indeed he ate and drank so fast,
　And used to stuff and cram,
The name they call'd him by at last
　Was often Greedy Sam.

The Letter.

WHEN Sarah's papa was from home a great way,
She attempted to write him a letter one day,

First ruling the paper, an excellent plan,
In all proper order Miss Sarah began.
She said she lamented sincerely to tell,
That her dearest mamma had been very unwell;
That the story was long, but that when he came
　back,
He would hear of the shocking behaviour of Jack.
Though an error or two we by chance may detect,
It was better than treating papa with neglect;
For Sarah, when older, we know will learn better,
And write single I with a capital letter.

Going to School.

GOOD children, when they're sent to school,
　Will never loiter on the way:
With them this is a constant rule,
　And not to stop to stare and play.

They never speak to any one
　Who talks when he should mind his task,
For dunces frequently have on
　A very black and frightful mask.

But when they've been at school all day,
　Their tasks and lessons finished; then
Their friends will give them leave to play,
　When they return from school again.

THE
SECOND CHAPTER
OF
ACCIDENTS
AND
Remarkable Events:
CONTAINING
CAUTION AND INSTRUCTION
FOR
CHILDREN.

LONDON:

PRINTED BY AND FOR DARTON AND HARVEY

GRACECHURCH-STREET.

1801.

The enraged Bear.

A few years since, the crew of a ship, in a boat, belonging to the whale fishery, shot at a bear, at a short distance, and wounded it. The animal, greatly enraged, swam towards the boat, and attempted to get on board, by placing its fore foot on the gunnel; being repulsed with a hatchet, it continued to swim after them till they arrived at the ship, when it immediately ascended the deck: as the crew had fled into the shrouds, it was pursuing them thither, when a shot, from one of them, laid it dead upon the deck.

The playful Tiger.

A young tiger was brought over, a few years since, in the Pitt East India ship, which admitted every kind of play to be used by the men and boys on board. It sometimes slept in the hammocs with the sailors, and would allow two or three of them to repose their heads upon its back, whilst it lay stretched out to sleep on the deck. It would climb about the ship like a cat, and play with a

The Boy and the Bucket.

In a country village, some few years since, there was a well upon the common, for the use of the inhabitants: a little boy, on a visit to his friends there, and to whom a well was a new thing, went with his sister to see it: the bucket, at that time, happened to be drawn up to the top of the well, and he ventured to stand up in it; the weight of his body soon set the bucket in motion, and he very gradually descended to the bottom of the well, holding by the rope. A farmer's man, at some distance, perceiving the handle of the winch to turn round, and seeing no person near to it, he came to examine into the cause, when, hearing the cries of the little boy in the well, he wound up the bucket and saved the child from a watery grave.

dog, that was on board the ship, in a diverting manner. When the ship came into the river Thames, a poor woman went on board to sell ginger-bread and cakes: the smell of these things brought the tiger to the spot, and he jumped on her shoulders, like a cat, took some of the cakes, and retired without hurting the woman, though she was greatly frightened. Not long after, some of the sailors had bought a piece of fresh beef, one of whom was for stewing it, whilst others were for roasting it; but before the dispute was settled, the tiger had taken it away and eaten it.

All in the Water.

A little boy, who was very fond of drawing his two sisters in a chaise, was one day running, at a great rate, on a gravel walk in the garden, when, going rather too near the side of a fish-pond, he found himself unable, with all his endeavours, to stop the chaise time enough to prevent its falling into the water, and, being on a declivity and losing his balance, they all fell in. The pond was not very deep, and they got out unhurt, though very much wetted.

Remarkable punishment.

In the Blue-coat School, founded by that youthful king, Edward the Sixth, in London and in Hertford, a youth was lately rewarded by the governors, for saving his money and victuals, for an aged parent in distress.

On the contrary, disobedient children have been as frequently punished in many remarkable ways. Absalom raised an army against his father; but, on the day of battle, as he rode upon a mule, his hair caught hold of the boughs of an oak, and the mule that was under him went away. In this situation he was killed by Joab, and other soldiers.

Child and Rabbit.

Many a kind parent has been delighted at seeing an infant playing with a kitten, or a puppy; some have even kept lambs, pigs, or rabbits in their houses, for the amusement of their children; and many have had to deplore the accidents that have been occasioned thereby. A bookbinder once kept a rabbit for his child to play with; they were frequently fed at the same time, and at others

slept together: but, one day, as the child was asleep, the rabbit got up to its face, and had begun to eat its nose! Alarmed by its cries, the parents ran to help it and found its face covered with blood. To this day, so great an aversion has the child to a rabbit, that it cannot be prevailed upon to touch one.

Cautions to Walkers in the Streets of London.

Never turn hastily round the corner of a street, by this some have been greatly hurt. One young woman, in so doing, ran against a porter's load, and nearly lost one of her eyes by the blow she received: but this was partly owing to the porter not being in his proper place, for he was *close* to the wall, when he should have been the *farthest* from it.

Avoid a crowd as much as may be; yet, when accidents occur, endeavour to assist the afflicted, if practicable;—when not so, retire.

Never look backward and continue walking forward; some persons have received violent blows by so doing.

Strangers should enquire at houses, or shop-keepers, for any place they may want to find, and not of persons in the street.

The Escape.

William Hewet, a cloth-worker of London, lived on London Bridge in the year 1530, and as his maid servant was diverting his child on the edge of an open window, it slipped out of her hands and fell into the Thames! His apprentice, whose name was Osborn, immediately jumped out of the shop-window into the river after the child; and to the great joy of many spectators brought it safe on shore. Her father became rich, was knighted, and afterwards chosen lord mayor of London. When his daughter arrived at the age of maturity she had many suitors, among whom was the Earl of Shrewsbury; but her father rejected every offer, and gratefully betrothed her to Osborn, who had saved her life at the hazard of his own; he was the ancestor of the Duke of Leeds.

The Third Chapter of Accidents

A great cry, but no harm done.

A gardener was one day driving his loaded cart, with his wife in it, up Fish-street Hill, in London; when nearly opposite the monument, the cart upset, and shot the poor woman and all the apples, pears, &c. into the road. As the streets were full of passengers, many of them screamed out for fear, lest the poor woman should have been hurt; but she escaped with only the fright, and telling her husband that before she got into the cart again, she should see that the plugs were fastened safely.

Some few years since, a ship at sea, caught fire, the whole crew of which was obliged to take to their boat. After beating about for many days in the ocean, having only a large blanket for a sail; their whole stock of provisions being gone, and sorely pressed by hunger, they came to the resolution of casting lots, which of them should first be killed for supplying the others with food. The lot happened to fall upon one who was greatly beloved by the whole of the crew; and then who should take his life away became another difficulty, it was, however, at last determined to bleed him to death: but, at the very instant the fatal incision was about to be made, one of the company espied a sail at a great distance. It proved to be a merchant-ship from England, which took in the unhappy sufferers, and brought most of them safe to land.

A gentleman's coach, with an arms and crest painted thereon, describing this story, with a very appropriate motto, used frequently to pass to and fro, in the city of London, about the year 1772.

Air Balloons.

In the European Magazine for 1785, is the following account of an aerial voyage....... " On the 31st of August, at half past three, Mr. Arnold*, his son, and Mr. Appleby, a master's mate on board the Kite cutter, (who had the courage to undertake the being let down with a parachute from the balloon when a mile high) endeavoured to perform their engagements to the public, with the balloon from St. George's Fields; but an unlucky accident happening, by the parachute catching hold of a rail, nearly turned the boat, in which they were, upside down, when Mr. Arnold fell out. Mr. Appleby was thrown out of the basket, which was fastened to the boat in order for him to have come down with the parachute; they then cut the cord, and Mr. Arnold's son ascended to a great height, and made a very fine appearance; but it soon after burst, and came down amazingly fast into the Thames, near Gun-dock, Wapping. Happily neither of them received any hurt."

*He had but one leg.

Extraordinary Leap.

A young man of Lancaster riding on the road not far distant from Egremont, was passed by a single-horse chaise, which occasioning the animal to be very unruly, it struck off on a full gallop, and coming upon Egremont bridge, was going with such fury, that, unable to retrieve himself, he leaped upon the battlements, which are upwards of four feet high. The rider, finding it impossible to retrieve, and seeing the improbability of saving either of their lives, had the instantaneous presence of mind to strike him on both sides with the spurs, and force him to take a clear leap. Owing to this precaution, he alighted upon his feet, and the rider firmly keeping his seat, held up the horse, till reaching the bottom, he leaped off. When we consider the height of the bridge, (twenty feet and an half perpendicular) and that there was not one foot depth of water in the bed of the river where they fell, it is really miraculous that they were not both stricken dead upon the spot. The only injury he received was a sprain in one foot, which confined him three days at his inn, the King's Arms, in Whitehaven. His horse had a slight wound in the stifle joint. Both are now perfectly well.

Further Account of Air-Balloons.

Of all the voyages in balloons, hitherto executed, the most daring one appears to be that of Dr. Jefferies and M. Blanchard, across the Straits from Dover, in England, to Guiennes, in France. In which excursion, after passing over several vessels, they found the balloon was descending, on which they threw out a sack and an half of ballast; but as it continued to descend,

they not only threw out all their ballast, but a number of books which they had with them, and all their provisions; indeed they almost stript themselves naked to lighten the car, and at length had the satisfaction to find that they were rising from the sea, and, as the machine rose very fast, they were carried to a greater height than they had been at any former part of their voyage. They descended safely, among some trees, in the forest of Guiennes.

The print before us shews the perilous situation of Major Money, who had fallen, with a balloon, into the sea, near Yarmouth, in Norfolk, from which he was rescued by the hands on board the Argus sloop, after being in the water five hours, in the summer of 1785.

Extract of a Letter from India.

" Yesterday morning, December 22, 1792, Mr. Downey, Lieut. Pyefinch, and poor Monro, (only son of Sir H. Monro) went on shore on Saugur Island, to shoot deer. We saw many tracks of them, as well as of tigers; at three we sat down to refresh ourselves, when we were told a fine deer was near us. Downey and I jumped up to take our guns, I had just laid hold of mine, when I heard a roar like thunder, and saw an immense tiger spring on Monro, who was sitting down; in a moment his head was in the beast's mouth, and he rushed into the jungle with him with great ease, every thing yielding to his strength. The only effort I could make was to fire at him, though the youth was then in his mouth; my companion then fired two shots, and I once more, and we had reason to think that the tiger was wounded. We retired from the jungle, and a few minutes after the poor youth came up to us, all over blood, and fell. We took him on our backs to the boat, and got every medical assistance for him from the Valentine Indiaman, but without effect."

Danger of Travelling in Foggy Weather.

As the stage from London to Stoke Newington was passing through Kingsland Road, on a very foggy night, the coach going too near to the side of a brick field, opposite to Haggerstone, the horses missed their footing, and fell, with the coach and passengers, down a very steep bank; the carriage and horses were literally overturned, but neither the passengers, coachman, or horses received any injury.

Feed and treat a Lion well.

Some keepers of wild beasts have been known to play with the lion, and even to chastise him at pleasure, which the animal seemed to bear with a sullen composure, but sometimes resents, as the following instance will show.

Labat, a French author, tells us of a gentleman who kept a young lion in his chamber, and employed a servant to attend it, who frequently mixed blows with caresses. This treatment continued for

some time; but, one morning, the master was awakened by a great noise in his room, and undrawing his curtains, he saw the lion growling over the body of the man, whom it had just killed, and separated his head from his body. The terror of the gentleman may be easily conceived; he flew out of the room, and had the lion secured.

Never play with Fire-arms.

So many fatal accidents have happened, by children playing with fire-arms, that parents and others cannot be too careful in keeping guns and pistols out of their reach. At one time we hear of a brother firing at his sister, a man at his wife, and of a youth killing his beloved friend, without either having any such intention. On the night of the late general illumination on account of peace, as Edward Thumbwood was passing along King street, Golden Square, a pistol was fired from the shop of a tradesman in that street; the pistol contained a wooden ruler, which entered his thigh. He was taken to St. George's Hospital, where he expired next day. It appeared that the tradesman's son had fired the pistol, and accidentally left the ruler in the barrel, having used it as a ramrod.

THE
BUTTERFLY'S BALL,
— and the —
GRASSHOPPER'S FEAST.

LONDON:

Printed for J. Harris, corner of
St Paul's Church Yard,
Jan.y 1.st 1807.

COME, take up your hats, and away let us haste
To the *Butterfly's* Ball and the *Grasshopper's*
Feast:

The Trumpeter, *Gadfly*, has summon'd the
Crew,
And the Revels are now only waiting for you.

So said little Robert, and pacing along,
His merry Companions came forth in a throng,
And on the smooth Grass, by the side of a Wood,
Beneath a broad Oak that for ages had stood,
Saw the Children of Earth, and the Tenants of Air,
For an Evening's Amusement together repair.

And there came the *Beetle*, so blind and so black,
Who carried the *Emmet*, his Friend, on his back.

And there was the *Gnat*, and the *Dragon-fly* too,
With all their Relations, Green, Orange, and
Blue.

And there came the *Moth*, with his plumage of
    down,
And the *Hornet*, in Jacket of Yellow and Brown,

Who with him the *Wasp*, his Companion, did
    bring,

But they promised that Evening to lay by their
    Sting.
And the sly little *Dormouse* crept out of his hole,
And brought to the Feast his blind Brother, the
    Mole.

And the *Snail*, with his Horns peeping out of his
    Shell,
Came from a great distance, the Length of an Ell.

A Mushroom their Table, and on it was laid
A Water-dock Leaf, which a Table-cloth made.
The Viands were various, to each of their taste,
And the *Bee* brought her Honey to crown the
    Repast.
Then close on his haunches, so solemn and wise,
The *Frog* from a corner look'd up to the Skies;
And the *Squirrel*, well pleased such diversions to
    see,
Mounted high over-head, and look'd down from a
    Tree.

Then out came the *Spider*, with finger so fine,
To shew his dexterity on the tight line.
From one branch to another, his Cobwebs he
    slung,
Then quick as an arrow he darted along;
But just in the middle,—Oh! shocking to tell,
From his Rope, in an instant, poor Harlequin fell.
Yet he touch'd not the ground, but with talons
    outspread,
Hung suspended in air, at the end of a thread.
Then the *Grasshopper* came with a jerk and a
    spring;
Very long was his Leg, though but short was his
    Wing;
He took but three leaps, and was soon out of
    sight,
Then chirp'd his own praises the rest of the night.
With step so majestic the *Snail* did advance,
And promised the Gazers a Minuet to dance.

But they all laugh'd so loud that he pull'd in his
    head,
And went in his own little chamber to bed.

Then, as Evening gave way to the Shadows of
    Night,
Their Watchman, the *Glow-worm*, came out with
    a light.

Then Home let us hasten, while yet we can see,
For no Watchman is waiting for you and for me.
So said little Robert, and pacing along,
His merry Companions return'd in a throng.

PLAIN THINGS FOR LITTLE FOLKS

THE OBEDIENT CHILD.

This docile little maiden shows
The worth of cleanliness she knows.

THE LITTLE SEMPSTRESS.

This pretty sempstress who can see
And not admire her industry
As thus upright she sits to sew,
Not stooping as some children do.

THE TENDER NURSE.

Our little nurse with pleasure eyes
Her Baby charge, and fondly tries
To wrap around its helpless form
Her shawl, to keep the darling warm.

This rustic maid enjoys her ride,
Her Donkeys sleekness is her pride:
If not the swiftest of his race
No beast can trot with surer pace.

COTTAGE BOY.

Humble in dress and low in state
Behold our peasant boy,
Yet think not his the hardest fate
Who wears the smile of joy.

No Pleasant task this picture to take,
Still worse in life a copy to make!

NURSE OUTWITTED.

Your best leg first good nurse I pray
For see how fast I run away ;
That pretty dress yourself may wear,
Nurse in a frock, will make folks stare.

THE YOUTHFUL GARDENER.

Young as our Gardener may appear
Yet do not spurn his care ;
His hand the drooping plants shall rear
And make them bloom more fair.

THE DUNCE.

This is a sight to give us pain,
Once seen ne'er wished to see again.

CATCHING A WHALE.

Good seamen strike with skill,
For should you miss your aim
Yon Whale knows how to fill
Your boat, and sink the same !

DRESSING A DOLL.

This is a baby Fanny cries ,
One may indeed caress,
Say what you will, she ne'er replies
Or is she proud of dress ;

THE LAUNCH IN MINIATURE.

No ship builder famed for his skill
Can feel more delighted than Will,
Thus launching his tight little ship
Prepared for a fresh water trip.

THE SISTERS:

AN INTERESTING TALE:

FOUNDED ON FACT.

PUBLISHED BY

EDWARD LACEY, 76, ST. PAUL'S CHURCH YARD,

LONDON.

THE sisters took away what flowers they could carry: their large nosegays contained many of the sweetest fragrance and the richest colours. They were delighted beyond expression in the purpose of disposing of them in the most tasteful manner, on the evening of the following day, about their mamma's bed and bed room, that she might awake on the morning of her birth-day amidst as beauteous a scene, and as odorous a smell, as art and nature combined could produce.

It had been the wish of their father, Mr. Fremolt, to delay his journey till after this anticipated and welcome day; but then he must have delayed receiving large sums of money, and large orders for spring goods—an injury which Mrs. Fremolt would, on no account, allow any thing relating to herself to occasion to their property. He took care, however, as he passed through the town, a few miles from his residence and manufactory, to order his banker to let his eldest daughter have a few pounds to expend, at her discretion, for the greater comfort and better celebration of the day in his absence. She was too discreet a child to abuse the trust, or to waste the money; though her inexperience might mistake the best methods of applying every part of it. The greater portion was expended in purchasing certain little delicacies, of which she knew her mamma to be particularly fond; but some went to procure a few perfumes of a remarkably strong, as well as sweet scent, which she had been told would preserve the odour of the flowers, and increase the fragrance of the chamber.

When the evening arrived, and the preparations were complete, Maria and her sister first threw open the windows of the room, because they found the odour stronger than they could at first well endure. The admission of the fresh air tempered the fragrance, and rendered it truly delightful; so that, when the hour of retirement drew near, every one—and several friends who had called that evening were requested to enter the chamber—acknowledged that it was altogether the most delightful and delicious retreat they had ever witnessed. The sisters were on the very summit of delight and anticipation, as they descended from the enchanting spot with the last party of friends, and heard their expressions of admiration,—" What a paradise! how exquisite the sight and the smell! Where can be a more perfect garden of beauty and fragrance! When was art ever found so skilfully blended with nature!"

The evening being fine and warm, the windows were kept open as late as possible; and, after supper, Mrs. Fremolt prayed with her affectionate daughters, blessed them in her fondest and devoutest manner, and proceeded, for the first time since its adornment, to her chamber of beauty and bliss—as she called it. The blending of nature's evening air with the artificial atmosphere of the shrubs and flowers was, as she entered the chamber door, truly delicious; while the lovely scene filled her with so much delight, that she was almost at a loss for words or strength. Turning to her children, who followed close behind her, she said,—" I must once more embrace and thank you. It far exceeds my utmost expectations, and is such a proof of your skill, as well as kindness, that my hopes of your improvement in every useful and ornamental art, consistent with your station and your sex, are raised to the very highest pitch. I seem now to have only one domestic wish left in my heart —that your dear father were here to breathe the balmy fragrance, and behold the exquisite beauty, which your affection has created. But this is the hour he appointed for retiring—*wherever he is*—to pray in secret for me. His chamber of devotion, I undertake to say, is not decorated like mine; but his prayers will not therefore be unavailing; you must now leave me, that I may spend the hour in prayer for him—*and for you,* whom he will not forget."

The delighted children were leaving their equally delighted mamma, when she stopped them a moment longer, to say—"I seemed to have but one domestic wish left, that your dear father were here; but as this is denied me, another has just sprung up and taken its place—it is, that you were both about to sleep with me for once, in this sweet chamber; but it is too late to remove your beds now, and I could neither accommodate you both, nor separate you from each other. However, it may be best as it is: a very slight partition will separate us, and your bed stands very near my own."

"We can sleep in your chamber to-morrow night," said Maria; "and, as for to-night, our bed shall be as near to yours as possible in five minutes. Before we lie down, we will move the head close to the partition, and just where yours comes on the other side. The nearer we are in death as well as life to you, dearest mamma, the better. We shall almost hear you breathe, and, should you have a dream that makes you talk at all, take care it is something you do not mind our hearing. And in the morning! in the morning! we shall rise as early as the lark—though we shall wait till we hear you preparing to rise before we enter your room, or make the least noise to disturb you."

"Blessed children!" said their delighted mother; "I can bear to hear no more—you must now go and rest your weary limbs, and dream of paradise, papa, and me."

Next morning the sisters were early preparing their mamma's birth-day breakfast. Papa's considerate bounty had enabled Maria to provide whatever she knew her mamma was likely to relish, and the table was spread before a single inquiry was made whether she had awoke. "Let me go now, and give a gentle tap at the chamber door," said Emily; and, before Maria could well answer her, more than a tap, and louder than a gentle one, was given without effect. "It was late, and dear mamma was fatigued when she went to bed," said Maria, "and we must allow her a little more sleep and a little more slumber; meanwhile let us fetch papa's portrait from his private room, and hang opposite the place where mamma will sit at breakfast."

The portrait had already been removed from its usual place to the bed room. Mrs. Fremolt had said to her servant, after Maria had left her, "As my dear husband is not here, I will at least have his likeness, to add all that can be added to the beauty of the room;" and the active servant had instantly fetched the portrait, and fixed it among the most handsome exhibitions of the flowers opposite the foot of the bed. "The young ladies, ma'am," said the servant, as she was making the portrait fast to the wall," will be surprised and pleased, indeed, when they find this in the morning! And you too will be delighted in having this the first thing to look at when you awake!"

Maria conjectured what had occasioned the usual place of the portrait to be vacant, and was sorry only because, in her anxiety about the flowers, she had overlooked this opportunity of adding to her mamma's delight. However, it was done; and for her now to fetch the portrait from the chamber to the breakfast parlour, would either awake her dear mamma before her time, or disappoint her of the first and welcome object of her morning vision.

"I long still," said the sisters to each other at the same moment, "to see how the portrait looks among the flowers."

"There was an excellent place for it," said Maria, "just under the principal garland, and the grand festoon. I am half tempted gently to open the door, and take a peep at papa amidst the flowers."

"Let me go first," said Emily, "and you can then look over my shoulder.—But did I not hear a step in the room?—is not some one stepping across it, and opening the door now? Perhaps while we talked, dear mamma rang the bell, and her faithful Jane immediately answered it. Hark, sister, either Jane or mamma herself is coming quickly out of the room.—What noise is that? there is something the matter!"

Just then it sounded to the sisters as though some one had fallen to the floor. The noise ceased in a moment, and they desired the other servant to go and see what had occasioned it. "Jane! Jane!" she immediately cried out; "what is the matter? are you ill, or have you hurt yourself?" By this time the sisters were at the top of the stairs, requesting Esther not to speak so loud, lest she should awake and alarm their mamma. The man-servant now came up, and said, "Jane is given to fainting fits, and I have no doubt the strong smell of the flowers has overcome her: let me carry her into her room." He did so, and she remained senseless more than half an hour, till the melancholy cause of her fainting became fully discovered.

"If the flowers have produced this effect upon poor Jane, we had better," said Maria, in a whisper, "gently open both the door and window, and refresh our dear mamma with a little of the morning air." She then gently stepped across the room, and, opening the window, returned as far as the picture—at which she looked for a minute, and then avoided the bed, lest she should disturb what she deemed her mamma's sound and sweet repose. But Emily had gone to the bed-side, and thought her mamma looked unusually pale. Leaning down her head to give one gentle kiss, she heard no breath! and, applying her lips to the cheek, it was cold as well as pale! She mentioned this to Maria, and the dismal truth pierced her breast in a moment. "O merciful God!" she cried, and sunk to the ground. Emily fell upon her sister in an agony of grief. The servants entered, and found their beloved and adored mistress in the sleep of death! She had fallen a victim to the affectionate attention of her dear girls.

To attempt to describe the scene would be fruitless. To tell the anguish and misery of the sisters, would be impossible. To describe what the bereaved husband and distracted father felt, would be equally beyond our power. The reader, however, must know, that it was a scene of real life, not thirty years ago!—that the husband could not long survive his irreparable loss—and that the sisters, though still living, continue to feel, in a large degree, the wretchedness of spirit this calamity occasioned—a wretchedness which no time, no society, nothing but their own death, is likely to remove or relieve.

JUVENILE FORGET ME NOT.
1830.

219

The Osborne Collection

In 1949, the Osborne Collection of Early Children's Books was presented to the Toronto Public Library by the eminent British librarian, Edgar Osborne, M.A., F.L.A., in memory of his wife, Mabel Osborne. Fifteen years earlier, Mr. and Mrs. Osborne had visited Canada and had been impressed with the public library services to children in this city. It occurred to them, then, that it might prove of benefit to Canadians engaged in library work with children or in writing and publishing children's books, if the collection they had been gathering together since 1920 could be made available to Boys and Girls House, the central children's library in Toronto.

After Mrs. Osborne's death in 1946, Mr. Osborne approached the Chief Librarian, Dr. Charles R. Sanderson, and offered to give his collection of 2,000 children's books published in England from 1566 to 1910 to the Toronto Public Library if the Board would assume the responsibility of enlarging and maintaining it, of publishing a printed catalogue and of making the collection accessible to the general public for research in this specialized field of English letters. These conditions have all been carried out. The Collection has been more than doubled in size for about 3,000 books have been acquired by the library through purchase or by gift. Mr. Osborne still takes an active interest in locating rare books and the Library Board is also indebted to many donors in Great Britain, the United States, and Canada who have helped to enrich the Collection.

A printed catalogue was published in 1958, produced by the University of Toronto Press, with a generous grant from the McLean Foundation of Toronto. It contains more than 3,000 entries describing books for children published from the days of Queen Elizabeth to the end of the reign of Edward VII. This catalogue has become a basic work of reference for persons concerned with English children's books and the detailed indexes to British printers, publishers and illustrators facilitate research into the whole scope and activity of the publishing industry for children.

Since the publication of the catalogue, visitors have come from all parts of the globe to see and to use the Collection. Scholars, bibliographers, book collectors, librarians, writers, artists, and students of children's literature, social sciences and education have found useful material locked within the covers of books which have been miraculously preserved from the destructive fate of most children's books.

The Board was happy to welcome Mr. Leonard de Vries in the summer of 1963 and to assist him in compiling the present work. Surrounded by many hundreds of books from which his selection was made, Mr. de Vries could take only a sample of the wealth of stories and illustrations of the period but enough to reveal a good deal about the juvenile 'reading public' of the period he has chosen to illustrate.

By the 1830's popular literacy had become a force to be reckoned with in the world of English writing and publishing. Sir Walter Scott observed at the time: 'Reading is . . . so general among all ranks and classes, that the impulse received by the public mind on such occasions is instantaneous . . . instead of being slowly communicated from one class to another, as was the case in the days of our fathers'. The Osborne Collection of Early Children's Books enables us to look back at some of the instruments of this transformation. *Flowers of Delight* is a reminder that such books and their illustrations are of vital interest in our study of the vanishing world of the eighteenth and nineteenth centuries. At the same time it provides us with early versions of some of the tales and stories that we still cherish.

Henry C. Campbell
Chief Librarian
Toronto Public Library
Toronto, Canada

March 30, 1965.

The Anthologist's Apology

Before explaining why, where and how I compiled this anthology I must confess that until 16 November 1957 I had never seen any old children's books and had never even given them a thought. On that day I asked at a children's library in my home town of Amsterdam for prewar juvenile books on science experiments. The librarian advised me to have a look at the antiquated children's books which were stored in the attic. In that cold, rather dim attic I found what I had asked for, met several good old friends—books I had read when I was a child—and nearly overlooked some dozens of little dusty booklets, which finally drew my attention mainly by their strange small size.

My curiosity aroused, I picked one up, leafed through it and soon found myself fascinated by this twelfth edition, anno 1833, of *De brave Hendrik*, once a bestseller, of which the title has survived because it became proverbial—a boy who is too much of a goody-goody, we call a 'brave Hendrik' in Holland. Delighted by this discovery I turned to the other old booklets. What would they contain? I felt like someone who sees a trace of gold glittering quite unexpectedly between mud and stones and can't help but start digging. It turned out that some of the other books were even more exciting than that first one; and this is how I fell in love with early children's books—love at first sight!

What happens when somebody stumbles upon something that delights him and arouses his enthusiasm? He wants to show it to other people. I was so impressed by these old children's books and I was sorry that they were not only *passé*, but also forgotten, that I wanted to make an anthology of them. After six months of research in various libraries in the Netherlands I published an anthology of early Dutch children's books under the title *Bloempjes der Vreugd*, which means 'Flowers of Joy'. This title was used in 1828 by Petronella Moens, who, though she had been blind from her early childhood, wrote many beautiful children's books.

The gayest book I had found, *De vermaarde*

historie van Gilles Zoetekoek of 1781, was a translation of an English book, *The Renowned History of Giles Gingerbread*, published about 1765 by John Newbery; the loveliest collection of poems after 1800 I had come across, *Veldviooltjes*, was a Dutch edition of *The Cowslip* by Elizabeth Turner. These two made me very curious about early English children's books. In Amsterdam University Library I was able to get hold of several books on this subject, but to my surprise I discovered that no anthology comparable to my *Bloempjes der Vreugd* existed. Therefore I decided to compile one. Perhaps this was somewhat pretentious for one who, though a writer of children's books, is after all a Dutchman and a foreigner. Should I apologize for that?

I went to London, to the British Museum, but it turned out that its many early children's books had never been catalogued as such. Then somebody told me about the existence of a large fully catalogued collection of early English children's books at the Toronto Public Library in Canada—the Osborne Collection—and put me in touch with Mrs. K. E. Endicott, a member of the staff of that library, who was in London. She was kind enough to lend me the book which since then has become my closest companion: the impressive 560-page catalogue of the Osborne Collection, so well prepared by Miss Judith St. John. This catalogue made it clear to me that the Osborne Collection was ideal for my purpose—and a good reason for a trip to Canada.

Would there be any chance of meeting Mr. Edgar Osborne, this ardent collector and former County Librarian of Derbyshire, who had generously donated his collection to the Toronto Public Library in 1949? Again I was in luck and a few days later I had the honour and pleasure of talking to Mr. Osborne himself—an inspiring experience!

Then, in 1963, I went to Canada on a quest as exciting and full of adventure as a true voyage of discovery.

The anthology *Flowers of Delight* has been

composed entirely from material selected from the Osborne Collection. About the origin of this collection Mr. Edgar Osborne wrote in his introduction to the catalogue:

It began on one of those all too rare occasions when I was able to return to my old home in Hampshire. There I found that the nursery books I loved so much were lying neglected in the lumber room. The discovery also interested my wife, who wondered if she would be able to rescue the books of her childhood from her home in the north of England. It was in this Yorkshire home that two volumes of the second edition of . . . *The Parent's Assistant* were found . . . Both these rare volumes came to light in the old nursery in Mabel Osborne's home, and this was indeed beginners' luck, for it was years afterwards before we discovered what a wonderful treasure we possessed. Thus began a partnership in collecting which continues to interest me, and which was of absorbing interest to my wife until her death in 1946.

How enjoyable it was to spend several months in the hospitable Toronto Public Library, engrossed in the early children's books—months of finding hidden treasures among the faded volumes. What these forgotten children's books reveal to us from the world of the past is so interesting and so colourful, moving, amusing, surprising or even perplexing, that they cried out to be rescued from oblivion. Therefore I brought together the pieces of prose and poetry that touched me most into this anthology. My standard of selection has been simply that I have chosen what I liked best myself—and I hope that many readers will enjoy these pieces as much as I do.

I limited myself to the period which, in my opinion, is the most fascinating and in certain respects the most beautiful one for children's books, not only in England but also in the Netherlands: the second half of the eighteenth century and the first thirty years of the nineteenth century. To explain why this period was so extraordinary, I must say something about the origin of children's books.

Until the end of the Middle Ages no books were written especially for children. These started to appear in the sixteenth century as a result of the Renaissance, Humanism, Reformation and an enlarged printing capacity. The first books actually written for children were books of instruction: schoolbooks, guides to conduct and manuals of religion. For reading lessons, translations and adaptations of classical fables such as Aesop's were used.

During the next two or three centuries the activity of the 'chapmen' played a very important part in fostering the popularity and distribution of books. These chapmen were pedlars, who travelled all over the country, selling among many other things inexpensive books that varied in price from a half-penny to sixpence. These 'chapbooks' were not bound in leather; they were 'paperbacks' of a small 'pocket' size, and they were often 'condensed' as well—reduced versions of longer originals. Many of them were in fact adaptations, suitable for children and poorly-educated country folk, of the fables already mentioned, of medieval romances like *Robin Hood*, of ballads and later of fairy tales, such as Perrault's *Tales of Mother Goose*, in which the English followed the fashion that had come from France. Shortly after the publication of Defoe's *Robinson Crusoe* in 1719 and Swift's *Gulliver's Travels* in 1726 chapbook versions came on the market, which quickly established their reputation as stories for children though they had not been written for children at all.

In the eighteenth century much of the popular literature of previous centuries became available in condensed form as chapbooks and some were adapted for use by children. They were so successful that until well into the nineteenth century chapbooks were *par excellence* the 'best-sellers' amongst children's reading-matter. And they deserved this success, even though many of them were badly printed on bad paper and some were written in an awkward style. The great merit of these chapbooks was that, being so inexpensive, they were within the reach of even the poorer families and thus brought literature into the hands of hundreds of thousands of children. In this respect they did a much better job than what forms, quantitatively, the main portion of children's reading-matter today: comics with their cheap content.

To honour these chapbooks I have included in this anthology facsimile reproductions of several chapbook versions of nursery rhymes, such as *A Apple-Pie*, *Mother Hubbard* and *Simple Simon*. That they may be distinguished from the other books in this anthology some have been printed on a different coloured paper. Most of the chapbooks reproduced sold for one penny or less and have only sixteen pages, being in fact one sheet folded in eight, without any cover. When folded, they measure about $2\frac{1}{2}$ to 4 inches along the longest side. Like so many of the chapbooks of the eighteenth and nineteenth centuries they are illustrated with woodcuts; some of these are rather crude, naive and primitive, but at the same time, aren't they charming and, in some cases such as *Cock Robin*, of an amazing graphic beauty? Yes, I am very fond of these modest little things.

Towards the middle of the eighteenth century the regular production of real children's books began. What are real children's books? F. J. Harvey Darton, in his unsurpassed standard work *Children's Books in England*, defines children's books as 'printed works produced ostensibly to give children spontaneous pleasure, and not primarily to teach them, nor solely to make them good, nor to keep them *profitably* quiet'. Of such children's books only a very few had so far been produced, but by then the time was ripe for them.

Several factors determined the climate in which children's literature in the sense of Darton's definition and of *belles lettres* could sprout and flower. One was that children were thought of less as small-sized adults and more as children. John Locke's great influence was largely responsible for this. In *Some Thoughts Concerning Education*, published 1693, this philosopher had declared: 'Children should be treated as rational creatures . . . They should be allowed liberties and freedom suitable to their ages . . . They must not be hindered from being children, nor from playing and doing as children . . . Curiosity is but an appetite after knowledge, the instrument nature has provided to remove ignorance'. These revolutionary new ideas were slowly but surely accepted. Later it was Rousseau—his *Emile ou de l'éducation* was published in 1762—whose fiery pleading for a more natural and harmonious education strongly stimulated the development of children's literature.

Another very positive factor was that in the eighteenth century England became a strong, prosperous nation, free of civil war, with close relations with the Continent, more world-minded and with a large, domesticated middle class. The prosperity, the internal peace, the increase in the

habit of reading, and the cheerful cultural life, all these created good circumstances for the start of children's books.

It was John Newbery who concentrated his deep and sincere love for children, his interest in literature and writers, his bursting energy in business enterprise and his probable great idealism into 'pretty things for little folks' and became the first successful publisher of children's books. A new era in education and literature began in 1744, when John Newbery published *A Little Pretty Pocketbook*, of which the expanded title stated that it was 'intended for the Instruction and Amusement of Little Master Tommy and Pretty Miss Polly, with an agreeable letter to read from Jack the Giant Killer, as also a Ball and a Pincushion the use of which infallibly make Tommy a good Boy, and Polly a good girl'. In this first book, which he probably wrote himself, he deliberately set out to provide amusement and he was not afraid to do so.

According to F. J. Harvey Darton this John Newbery, 'the philanthropic bookseller in St. Paul's Churchyard', published, up to his death in 1767, about twenty children's books, which fell more or less satisfactorily within Darton's definition, but perhaps there were more. Such a children's list was something entirely new in the English book trade. The same goes for his working methods. Many of these books he 'invented' himself. He chose able literary men with an understanding of children to write them and maintained close and very friendly relations with his authors. He paid great attention to every detail of production, from good typography and illustrations to the best format, printing and binding. Whomsoever he employed, his own charming personality was reflected in each of the books he published. Children and parents liked these low priced, nice looking volumes with their pleasant contents and, because John Newbery was such a good businessman as well, his enterprise was a complete success. He had convincingly demonstrated the great possibilities in publishing for children and his success encouraged other publishers to follow his example. It is from their books that *Flowers of Delight* has been composed.

I intend to make a second anthology in which John Newbery's epochal publications are given fully the space and the honour they deserve. However, *Flowers of Delight* does include one of the finest examples of Newbery's rich legacy: a later chapbook version of *The Renowned History of Giles Gingerbread*, a book first published by Newbery about 1765. It is probable that it was written by John Newbery himself—and it certainly reflects the spirit of this great friend of children in the best possible way.

Flowers of Delight covers the period 1765-1830, beginning at the end of John Newbery's time and ending seven years before the start of the Victorian age. What most children's books published between 1765 and 1830 have in common, and what distinguishes them from the later ones, is their small size—they average 4 to 6 inches along the longest side—and their harmonious typographical design; the very characteristic styles of their illustrations; the anonymity of their authors (though the names of several of them have been traced) and the fact that many of their authors can be considered as disciples of Locke or Rousseau; their fresh, idealistic and enthusiastic spirit; and a degree of realism from which most present-day authors of children's books shrink. Every year thousands of children are killed or crippled in road accidents, but generally speaking the writers of our children's books act as if this danger did not exist at all, even though they could save many children's lives by mentioning it occasionally. In many early children's books the authors did try to save children's lives by telling frankly about the dangers of life. The 'happy ending', often so untruthful and illogical, was not yet a 'must' as it has become in nearly all twentieth-century children's books.

Another characteristic of many of the children's books of the period 1765-1830 is their determined attack upon injustice and oppression. They tell their young readers the unvarnished truth about such social abuses as child labour and slavery. The men and women who wrote them were warmly human and had high ideals. They set themselves with heart and soul to the task of giving the children the best of the best. In this goal they were firmly supported by the illustrators, printers and binders, who exerted themselves to make their publications veritable little jewels. Many woodcuts and engravings on wood or copper of this period are of unequalled charm and beauty. The colouring of them by hand was mostly done by poor families in their own homes.

Until about 1830 this high level was maintained—though there were inevitably a number of markedly inferior books which in general have not survived into the big collections of today. Then came the decline. This was due to the supersession of handwork by machines; faster printing techniques which lowered the prices but also the quality; the invention of chromolithography, which made colour printing possible, unfortunately with mostly ugly results; the heavy commercialization of the children's book trade; the striving after mass-production and the explosion of bad taste which marked the greater part of the nineteenth century.

For several decades the average level of illustrations and typographical design of most of the children's books was low. In the eighties came an improvement, partly because of the activities of such artists as Randolph Caldecott and Kate Greenaway, so favourably influenced by their printer, Edmund Evans. Nevertheless in the Victorian period children's books of great literary and artistic value appeared such as Lewis Carroll's masterpiece *Alice's Adventures in Wonderland* (1865).

Anyway, the children's books published between 1765 and 1830 are so different from those published in the next half-century and in their get-up so superior that they show to the fullest advantage in an anthology devoted entirely to them. In certain respects there is wide variation between individual books, particularly in the style of illustration; compare, for instance, the antiquated style of *Scripture Histories* (1825—the woodcuts are probably older) with the very advanced style of *The Butterfly's Ball* (1807). Nevertheless there is such a general harmony among most of the books of this period that they can fairly be regarded as a unity; and I have not felt it either necessary or desirable to arrange the fragments from them into a chronological sequence.

'England could be reconstructed entirely from its children's books', wrote Paul Hazard. In this exaggeration there is much truth. One of the main attractions of these early children's books is that they give so much inside information concerning England from 1765 to 1830, not second-hand, explained over and over again as history books do, but first-hand, thus enabling every reader to draw his own conclusions. This is the reason I do not offer any comment on the individual books which have gone into the making of this anthology—they speak for themselves. Biographical data on some of their writers, illustrators and publishers will be found on page 231.

Some of the original books used for *Flowers of Delight* are in a bad condition, worn out by being read by children again and again, soiled, scratched, damaged, stained by damp, or just badly printed. *The Courtship and Marriage of Jerry and Kitty*, reproduced in colour on pages 25-28, is a good example of such a battered booklet. Consequently if some of the illustrations in this anthology appear to fall below standard it is because of this. In general the reproductions are about the same size as the originals; those on the jacket, the endpapers, on pages 30-35, 51-54, 103-106 and 154-156 and the frontispiece, however, have been enlarged. On pages 21, 22, 24, 69-75, 87-90, 99-101, 110-116, 138-142, 167-173, 184 and 205 some of the illustrations belong to the quoted book, but not to the stories or poems quoted. As is mentioned in the Notes, three illustrations used (on page 93 and page 116) come from other books. The typography of this anthology is not entirely consistent in that as far as possible the typographical style of the original books—i.e. double quotations at the beginning of each line of a passage of dialogue—has been followed. Everywhere the original spelling and punctuation have been followed. In some cases prose selections have been shortened.

I strongly urge anyone who is interested in the history of English children's books to read the three books from which I have derived much of my knowledge: the already mentioned *Children's Books in England* by F. J. H. Darton, Percy Muir's very interesting and beautifully illustrated *English Children's Books* 1600 *to* 1900, and the American work, *A Critical History of Children's Literature* by Cornelia Meigs, Elizabeth Nesbitt, Anne Eaton and Ruth Hill Viguers. *The Oxford Dictionary of Nursery Rhymes* compiled and edited by Iona and Peter Opie is also excellent. Details of these and other books on the history of English children's books are given in the Bibliography on page 232.

In conclusion I wish to express my thanks to Mr. Henry C. Campbell, Chief Librarian of the Toronto Public Library, who gave me from the first moment we met so much hospitality and every possible co-operation, to Mr. Wallace Bonner and many other members of the Library staff, to Mr. Bram Verhoeff and Mr. Kenneth McEvoy, who helped me with the enlarging of the photo reproductions I had made, to Mr. James Mosley of the St. Bride's Library in London, the source of the typographical flowers and borders for this anthology, to the Ansco Laboratory in Amsterdam, to Mr. Jan Tholenaar, who constructed such a fine reproduction apparatus for me, to the technical staff of The Ysel Press Ltd., Deventer, Holland, who printed *Flowers of Delight*, and to Miss Judith St. John, the librarian in charge of the Osborne Collection, to whose profound knowledge and sympathetic helpfulness I could so often make an appeal.

Leonard de Vries

Amsterdam, 29 April 1965

Notes on the Original Books

The bibliographical and biographical information has been taken from the Catalogue of the Osborne Collection of Early Children's Books and some annotations have been quoted in full with the permission of the Chief Librarian of the Toronto Public Library.

Vignette on endpapers from THE AFFECTION-ATE PARENT'S GIFT, and the good child's reward; consisting of a series of poems and essays, on natural, moral and religious subjects; calculated to lead the tender minds of youth in the early practice of virtue and piety, and thereby promote their temporal prosperity and eternal happiness. To which is prefixed, an affectionate address on the duties and obligations they owe to God and their parents. By Henry Sharpe Horsley. Illustrated by upwards of one hundred and fourteen engravings. London: Printed for T. Kelly by J. Rider, 1828. Two volumes in twenty-eight parts. 14.4 x 11 cm.

Half-title vignette from ACKERMANN'S JUVENILE FORGET-ME-NOT; a Christmas, New Year's and birthday present, for youth of both sexes. London: Ackermann [ca.] 1830. 13.9 x 8.7 cm.

Frontispiece from A COURSE OF LECTURES FOR SUNDAY EVENINGS. Containing religious advice to young persons. London: Printed and sold by John Marshall [1783?]. Pp. xvi, 124. 14.8 x 9.2 cm.
Probably by Mary Jane (Maze) Kilner (b. 1753). The copperplate frontispiece, engraved by T. Cook after Daniel Dodd, is dated 1783.

THE CHILDREN IN THE WOOD: a tale for the nursery. With copper-plates. A new edition. London: William Darton, jun., 1819. Pp. 32. 13.4 x 8 cm.
For centuries this story, known also as The babes in the wood, *was a favourite of troubadours and story-tellers. It appeared in book form in 1595 and it has been continuously reprinted ever since. Some authorities suggest that there might be a connection between it and the murder of the little princes in the Tower of London in 1483.* 9-13

Easy lessons from THE PARLOUR TEACHER. London: Printed by W. Darton and J. Harvey. Published as the act directs Sept. 14th 1804. Pp. [36]. 14.8 x 9.2 cm. 13

STORIES OF INSTRUCTION AND DELIGHT. London: Printed and sold by John Marshall [1802]. Pp. 60. 11 x 8.8 cm. 14-17

SELECT RHYMES FOR THE NURSERY, with copperplate engravings. London: Printed by and for Darton and Harvey, 1808. Pp. 48. 15.3 x 9.2 cm.
Written and illustrated by Jane Taylor, 1783-1824, and Ann (Taylor) Gilbert, 1782-1866. 18-24

THE COURTSHIP AND MARRIAGE OF JERRY & KITTY; illustrated with elegant engravings. London: Published Nov. 20-1814, by J. Harris. Ff. 15. 12.5 x 10.2 cm. 25-28

FILIAL DUTY, recommended and enforc'd, by a variety of instructive and entertaining stories, of children who have been remarkable for affection to their parents; also an account of some striking instances of children, who have behaved in an undutiful, and unnatural manner to their parents. The whole founded on historical facts. London: Printed for F. Newbery [ca. 1770]. Pp. viii, 165. 11.2 x 7.1 cm. 29

THE GOOD CHILD'S DELIGHT; or, The road to knowledge, in short entertaining lessons of one and two syllables. London: Printed and sold by John Marshall and co. [ca. 1785]. Pp. 84. 10 x 8.4 cm.
By Dorothy Kilner, 1755-1836. 30-35

Things by their right names from EVENINGS AT HOME; or, The juvenile budget opened. Consisting of a variety of miscellaneous pieces, for the instruction and amusement of young persons.

London: Printed for J. Johnson, 1792-96. Six volumes in three. 13.9 x 8.5 cm.
By John Aikin, 1747-1822, and Anna Laetitia (Aikin) Barbauld. 1743-1825. 35

LITTLE RHYMES FOR LITTLE FOLKS; or, A present for Fanny's library, by a lady. Second edition. London: J. Harris, 1823. Ff. 17. 17.5 x 10.7 cm. 36-39

EARLY SEEDS TO PRODUCE SPRING FLOWERS, by Mary Elliot. A new edition, corrected and revised. With copper-plates. London: William Darton [1824]. Pp. 24. 17 x 9.8 cm. 40-44

THE DAISY; or, Cautionary stories, in verse. Adapted to the ideas of children, from four to eight years old. With thirty engravings on wood. The twenty-first edition. London: John Harris; Simpkin, Marshall, and co.; J. S. Hodson; and Darton and Clark [ca. 1840]. Pp. 66. 13.7 x 8.8 cm.
By Elizabeth Turner, d. 1846. First published in 1807. The illustrations are drawn and engraved on wood by Samuel Williams. 45-50

THE HISTORY OF GILES GINGERBREAD, a little boy, who lived upon learning. By Tom Trip [pseud.]. Decorated with cuts. York: Printed and sold by J. Kendrew [1820 ?]. Pp. 31. 9.9 x 6.3 cm.
An abridged chapbook version of The renowned history of Giles Gingerbread, *which was published about 1765 by John Newbery. It was probably written by John Newbery, who is described in Oliver Goldsmith's* The vicar of Wakefield *as 'the philanthropic bookseller in St. Paul's Churchyard who . . . was at that time actually compiling material for the history of one Mr. Thomas Trip'. It has also been ascribed to Goldsmith himself, and to Giles Jones.* 51-54

Sixteen pence etc. from PENCE TABLE PLAYFULLY PARAPHRASED by Peter Pennyless [pseud.]. London: John Harris, 1818. Ff. 16. 11.8 x 9.4 cm 55-56

A PRESENT FOR A LITTLE GIRL. London: Printed and Sold by Wm. Darton & Josh. Harvey, Decr. 26th, 1797. Pp. [32]. 15.2 x 10 cm.
Written by William Darton, 1755-1819. The illustrations were drawn and engraved by the author. 57-60

INSTRUCTIVE HINTS, in easy lessons for children. Part II. London: Printed by and for Darton and Harvey, 1806. Pp. 48. 15.1 x 9.1 cm. 61-64

Inadvertent deceit from THE FEMALE GUARDIAN. Designed to correct some of the foibles incident to girls, and supply them with innocent amusement for their hours of leisure. By a lady . . . London: Printed and sold by John Marshall and co., 1784. Pp. x, 128. 15.2 x 9 cm.
By Lady Eleanor (Frere) Fenn, 1743-1823. 64

THE TRAGICAL DEATH OF A APPLE-PYE, who was cut in pieces and eat by twenty five gentlemen with whom all little people ought to be very well acquainted. London, Printed by John Evans [ca. 1791]. Pp. 16. 9 x 5.5 cm. 65

THE KNIFE-GRINDER'S BUDGET OF PICTURES FOR BOYS AND GIRLS. London: Printed for T. and J. Allman, 1829. Pp. 27. 8.8 x 5.7 cm. 66-67

THE HISTORY OF SAM, THE SPORTSMAN, AND HIS GUN, ALSO OF HIS WIFE JOAN. Embellished with wood-cuts. York: Printed and sold by J. Kendrew [ca. 1820]. Pp. 16. 9.6 x 6.5 cm. 68

THE BOOK OF GAMES; or, A history of juvenile sports, practised at the Kingston Academy. Illustrated by twenty-four copper-plates. London: Printed by J. Adlard for Tabart and co., 1805. Pp. 156. **13.4 x 8.3 cm.** 69-75

THE TALKING BIRD; or, Dame Trudge and her parrot. London: Printed for J. Harris, 1808. Pp. vi, 15. 11.8 x 9.4 cm.
First published in 1806. 76-79

PETER PIPER'S PRACTICAL PRINCIPLES OF PLAIN AND PERFECT PRONUNCIATION. To which is added, A collection of moral and entertaining conundrums. London: Printed for J. Harris and son, 1820. Pp. 34. 17.8 x 10.8 cm.
First published in 1813. Harris's Cabinet of amusement and instruction, no. 8. 80-85

DAME TRUELOVE'S TALES, now first published as useful lessons for little misses & masters, and ornamented with appropriate engravings. London, Published by J. Harris [1817]. Pp. 79. 12.3 x 9.4 cm. 86-90

THE PARENTAL INSTRUCTOR; or, A father's present to his children. Embellished with wood engravings. Edinburgh: Oliver and Boyd: Sold also by G. and W. B. Whittaker, London; and W. Turnbull, Glasgow [1820 ?]. Pp. 84. 13.6 x 8.7 cm. 91-93

The dangers of swimming from THE LITTLE TEACHER, for reading and spelling well. By a parent. London: Printed and sold by Darton and Harvey, 1798. Pp. [84]. 14 x 8.8 cm.
The upper cut on page 93 is from Instructive hints, *see page 61.* 93

THE ALPHABET OF GOODY TWO SHOES; with spelling and reading lessons. London: Grant and Griffith [ca. 1845]. Ff. 14. 18 x 10.5 cm.
First published by John Harris about 1820. 94-97

THE CHILD'S INSTRUCTOR; intended as a first book, for children, with superior engravings. By a fellow of the Royal Society. Fourth edition. Deal, Printed and sold by T. Hayward; London: Published by Messrs. Thorp and Burch, 1828. Pp. 69. 13 x 8.6 cm. 98

IDLE HOURS EMPLOYED; or, The new publication. A selection of moral tales. London: John Harris [1826]. Pp. 236. 16.8 x 10.2 cm.
99-102

The history of Sweetpea from THE HISTORY OF THE FAMILY AT SMILEDALE, presented to all little boys and girls who wish to be good, and make their friends happy. London: Printed for E. Newbery [ca. 1790]. Pp. 128. 10.6 x 7 cm.
102-103

SCRIPTURE HISTORIES; from the creation of the world, to the death of Jesus Christ. With a description of St. Paul's church, London. Decorated with cuts. Wellington: Printed by F. Houlston and son [ca. 1825]. Pp. 21. 10.2 x 6.4 cm.
103-104

AN ELEGY ON THE DEATH AND BURIAL OF COCK ROBIN. Ornamented with cuts. York: Printed by J. Kendrew [ca. 1820]. Pp. 16. 9.5 x 6.5 cm. 105-106

Here we go and *Here's the tailor with his shears* from THE WAGGON LOAD OF MONEY. A new invented little book, For little boys and girls in it to look: And when they've read it through they'll say, There [sic] money was not thrown away. York: Printed and sold by James Kendrew [ca. 1820]. Pp. 16. 9.5 x 6.5 cm. 106

THE HISTORY OF LITTLE TOM TUCKER. York: J. Kendrew [ca. 1820]. Pp. 16. 10 x 6.5 cm.
107-108

Jolly Welchman, Little Husband and *The Brown Cow* from THE CHEERFUL WARBLER, or, Juvenile song book. York: Printed and sold by J. Kendrew [ca. 1820]. Pp. 16. 9.8 x 6.4 cm. 108

RURAL SCENES, or, A peep into the country. For children. London: Printed for Harvey & Darton [1826]. Pp. 60. 15 x 9.5 cm.
By Jane Taylor, 1783-1824 *and Ann (Taylor) Gilbert,* 1782-1866. *The two upper cuts on page* 116 *are from* City Scenes, *see page* 166. 109-116

Mistress Towl, Old woman of Bath, Old Woman

of Croydon, Old Woman of Ealing, Old Woman of Lynn, Old Woman of Harrow, Old Woman of Exeter and *Old Woman of Gosport* from THE HISTORY OF SIXTEEN WONDERFUL OLD WOMEN, illustrated by as many engravings; exhibiting their principal eccentricities and amusements. Much credit is due to our artist, I ween; for such pictures as these can seldom be seen. London: Printed for Harris and son, 1820. Ff. 16. 17.6 x 10.6 cm.
Harris's Cabinet of amusement & instruction, no. 15. *The first known book of limericks, published twenty-six years before those of Edward Lear. With Anecdotes and adventures of fifteen gentlemen these verses may also have inspired Lear.* 117-118

THE AFFECTIONATE PARENT'S GIFT, and the good child's reward; consisting of a series of poems and essays, on natural, moral and religious subjects; calculated to lead the tender minds of youth in the early practice of virtue and piety, and therefore promote their temporal prosperity and eternal happiness. To which is prefixed, an affectionate address on the duties and obligations they owe to God and their parents. By Henry Sharpe Horsley. Illustrated by upwards of one hundred and fourteen engravings. London: Printed for T. Kelly by J. Rider, 1828. Two volumes in twenty-eight parts. 14.4 x 11 cm.
119-129

MEMOIRS OF THE LITTLE MAN AND THE LITTLE MAID: with some interesting particulars of their lives never before published. London: Published by B. Tabart, 1807. Pp. 12. 12.8 x 11.2 cm.
A preliminary note reads: 'This original and entertaining work will speedily be set to music by an eminent composer.' An extended version of the nursery rhyme attributed by Horace Walpole in 1764 *to Sir Charles Sidley.* 130-133

WHITTINGTON AND HIS CAT. London: John Harris [ca. 1825]. Ff. 17. 16.8 x 10.2 cm.
134-137

NURSERY MORALS, chiefly in monosyllables; with twenty-four engravings. By the author of "Always happy", &c., &c. . . . Third edition. London: Printed for J. Harris, 1825. Pp. vii, 165. 13.9 x 8.7 cm.
By Maria E. (Halsey) Budden, 1780?-1832. *The author wrote these short moral stories for her own and her sister's children. The dedicatory letter is dated from London,* 1818. 138-142

THE CHILD'S BOOK ON THE SOUL. With questions adapted to the use of Sunday schools, and of Infants' schools. By the Rev. T. H. Gallaudet. London: Published by L. B. Seeley and sons, 1832. Pp. viii, 114; vi, 138. 12.8 x 10.3 cm.

First published in Hartford, Connecticut, in 1830.
143-144

MOTHER HUBBARD AND HER DOG: to which is added, The history of Tom Tucker. Derby: Printed by and for Thomas Richardson [*ca.* 1830]. Pp. 27. 10.4 x 6.5 cm. 145-146

THE JUVENILE GAZETTEER. Derby: Printed by and for Thomas Richardson [*ca.* 1830]. Pp. 26. 9.9 x 6.4 cm. 147-148

LITTLE TRUTHS for the instruction of children. London: Printed and sold by Darton and Harvey, 1802. Two volumes. 11.7 x 7.7 cm.
By William Darton, 1755-1819. 149-153

The History of Jack the giant killer from JACK THE GIANT KILLER, a hero celebrated by ancient historians. Banbury: Printed by J. G. Rusher [*ca.* 1820]. Pp. 15. 8.7 x 6 cm. 153-156

AN ALPHABETICAL ARRANGEMENT OF ANIMALS FOR LITTLE NATURALISTS by Sally Sketch [*pseud.*]. From this nice book I plainly see You all must learn A.B.C.D. [London]. Published Jany. 1st 1821, by Harris & son. Ff. [28]. 12.3 x 10.5 cm. 157-158

Easy lessons from EASY LESSONS FOR YOUNG CHILDREN. Sixth edition. London: Printed for J. Johnson, 1807. Pp. v, 106. 9.6 x 8.3 cm.
By Sarah (Kirby) Trimmer, 1741-1810. 159

Three cuts from A PRESENT FOR INFANTS. London: Darton, Harvey & Darton, 1814. Ff. [24]. 15.7 x 9.6 cm.
A picture book without letterpress. The copper-plates were probably drawn and engraved by William Darton, 1755-1819. 159

LITTLE ABEL; or, The young orphan. An affecting tale. With, The story of Amelia. London: Printed for A. K. Newman & co., 1821. Pp. 21. 12.9 x 8.3 cm.
The wood engravings that illustrate this story were used at least twenty years earlier to illustrate The history of Jack and his eleven brothers. 160-162

OLD FRIENDS IN A NEW DRESS; or, Familiar fables in verse. London: Harvey and Darton; and William Darton, 1820. Pp. 46. 13 x 8.4 cm.
By Richard Scrafton Sharpe, d. 1852. 162-165

CITY SCENES; or, A peep into London for children. London. Printed and sold by Darton, Harvey & Darton, 1818. Pp. 72. 15 x 9.3 cm.
By Jane Taylor, 1783-1824 *and Ann (Taylor) Gilbert,* 1782-1866. *First written in* 1801 *by William Darton who also drew and engraved the*

copper-plates. It was revised by Jane and Ann Taylor in 1806 *with the illustrations drawn and engraved by Jane Taylor.* 166-173

THE BLACK MAN'S LAMENT; or, How to make sugar. By Amelia Opie [1769-1853]. London: Printed for Harvey and Darton, 1826. Ff. 20, pp. 21-25. 17.2 x 10.4 cm. 174-177

LITTLE JACK OF ALL TRADES, with suitable representations. London: Printed and sold by Darton and Harvey, 1806. In two parts. 15 x 9.6 cm.
In all probability both written and illustrated by William Darton, 1755-1819. 178-183

A pleasing and instructive story from PLEASING AND INSTRUCTIVE STORIES FOR YOUNG CHILDREN. By Mary Hughes (late Robson). London: William Darton, 1821. Pp. 105. 13.8 x 8.4 cm. 184

THE HISTORY OF SIMPLE SIMON. York: Printed by J. Kendrew [*ca.* 1820]. Pp. 16. 9.5 x 6.5 cm. 185-186

Riddle from A COLLECTION OF BIRDS & RIDDLES. By Miss Polly & Master Tommy. York: J. Kendrew [*ca.* 1820]. Pp. 16. 9.6 x 6.4 cm. 186

Wine and Cakes, Drummer and Sot, and *Little Man and Maid* from THE CHEERFUL WARBLER, or, Juvenile song book. York: Printed and sold by J. Kendrew [*ca.* 1820]. Pp. 16. 9.8 x 6.4 cm. 186 and 188

THE LIFE OF JACK SPRAT, HIS WIFE AND HIS CAT. York: Printed by J. Kendrew [*ca.* 1820]. Pp. 16. 9.4 x 6.5 cm. 187-188

THE RATIONAL EXHIBITION FOR CHILDREN. London: Printed by Darton and Harvey, 1800. March 8th. Pp. [72]. 14.6 x 8.6 cm. 189-195

THE PATH OF LEARNING STREWED WITH ROSES; or, The elements of English grammar. Illustrated by coloured engravings. London: Printed and sold by John Marshall, 1821. Ff. [16]. 18.2 x 11.2 cm. 196-197

THE SCHOOL GIRL: a poem, by William Upton. Illustrated with coloured engravings. London: William Darton [1820]. Ff. [6]. 12.8 x 10 cm. 198

THE COWSLIP, or More cautionary stories in verses, adapted to the capacities of children at an early age. By the author of "The Daisy". With thirty engravings. London: Grant and Griffith, successors to John Harris; Simpkin, Marshall,

and co.; J. S. Hodson; and Darton and co. [ca. 1850]. Pp. 67. 13.7 x 8.9 cm.
By Elizabeth Turner, d. 1846. The illustrations were drawn and engraved on wood by Samuel Williams in 1830. First published in 1811. 199-205

THE SECOND CHAPTER OF ACCIDENTS AND REMARKABLE EVENTS: containing caution and instruction for children. London: Printed by and for Darton and Harvey, 1801. Pp. [52]. 12 x 8.1 cm.
By William Darton, 1755-1819. In her Guardian of education, volume I, Mrs. Trimmer praises the engravings, criticizes the odd sort of composition, but observes: 'With a little previous inspection to obliterate such parts as may make hurtful impressions and weaken the minds of children, the books may be used, by a judicious parent, with advantage, as lessons to exercise learners in the art of reading'. 206-208

THE THIRD CHAPTER OF ACCIDENTS AND REMARKABLE EVENTS: containing caution and instruction for children. Philadelphia: Published by J. Johnson, 1807. Pp. 52. 12.8 x 8 cm.
By William Darton, 1755-1819. 208-211

THE BUTTERFLY'S BALL, AND THE GRASSHOPPER'S FEAST. London: Printed for J. Harris, Jany. 1st, 1807. Ff. [16]. 12.5 x 9.2 cm.
By William Roscoe, 1753-1831. The engraved text is above the fourteen uncoloured copperplates engraved after William Mulready. For Flowers of Delight the revised text of the 1808 edition has been used. 212-214

PLAIN THINGS FOR LITTLE FOLKS; seasoned with instruction both for the mind and the eye. By their friend Mary Elliot. London: William Darton and son [ca. 1830]. Pp. 23. 17 x 9.9 cm.
First published in 1814. The hand-coloured copper-engravings bear the date 1823. A companion to Early seeds to produce spring flowers, *see page* 40. 215-216

THE SISTERS: an interesting tale: founded on fact. London: Published by Edward Lacey. [ca. 1830]. 13.8 x 8.6 cm.
By Clara Hall. 217-219

Tail-piece of *Juvenile Forget Me Not* 1830 from ACKERMANN'S JUVENILE FORGET-ME-NOT; a Christmas, New Year's and birthday present, for youth of both sexes. London: Ackermann. [ca. 1830]. 13.9 x 8.7 cm. 219

Cut of boy reading to his mother from THE MOTHER'S GIFT. By a lady. York: Printed by J. Kendrew [ca. 1820]. Pp. 15. 9.6 x 6.5 cm. 232

Some Writers, Illustrators and Publishers

WILLIAM DARTON, 1755-1819. A Quaker who established a printing and publishing business at 55 Gracechurch Street, London, with Joseph Harvey about 1785. William Darton was not only a successful publisher, but also a talented engraver who illustrated and compiled several children's books.

MARY (BELSON) ELLIOTT. A Quaker who wrote under her maiden name, Mary Belson, until her marriage about 1818 or 1819. A popular and prolific writer of children's books.

LADY ELEANOR (FRERE) FENN, 1743-1813. Lady Fenn, a woman of great intellect, was inspired by Mrs. Trimmer and was interested in the education of children. She started a school where girls were taught to mend and patch clothing. She first wrote books for her brother's children, printed them herself and bound them in gaily-coloured paper.

THOMAS HOPKINS GALLAUDET, 1787-1831. Descended from French Huguenots who settled in New York. He graduated from Yale and studied for the ministry, but ill health prevented him from accepting a post. He became acquainted with a deaf child and after studying methods of education for the deaf, opened the first school for the deaf in the United States in 1817. He continued as Principal until 1830. He was also interested in the education of Negroes. He married a deaf pupil.

JOHN HARRIS: see under John Newbery.

JOHN NEWBERY, 1713-1767. When John Newbery was sixteen, he left the small Berkshire village where he was born and journeyed to Reading where he found employment with the printer and bookseller, William Carnan. After Carnan's death in 1737, Newbery married his widow and in 1744 moved to London, where he set up a business at the Bible and Crown, moving the following year to the Bible and Sun in St. Paul's Churchyard where he became 'a merchant in medicine as well as of books'. He specialized in Dr. James' Fever Powder and in the writing and publishing of books for children. When he died in 1767 he left part of his business to his son, Francis, in partnership with his stepson, Thomas Carnan and part to his nephew, *Francis Newbery*, who set up a bookshop at the corner of St. Paul's Churchyard. After the death of Francis in 1780, his widow *Elizabeth Newbery* (1746-1821) continued to run the business until her retirement in 1801 when it was taken over by her manager *John Harris* (1756-1846). Harris had worked with John Murray before entering Mrs. Newbery's firm. He maintained the Newbery tradition of specializing in children's books.

AMELIA (ALDERSON) OPIE, 1769-1853. Her father was a popular physician of Norwich. She married the artist, John Opie in 1798 and he encouraged her to write. Her husband died in 1807 and Mrs. Opie returned to Norwich to live with her father. She became a Quaker in 1825 and interested herself in prison reform, slavery and works of charity.

WILLIAM ROSCOE, 1753-1831. An historian, a banker, a botanist, a noted book-collector, an attorney, and a member of Parliament. He has been acclaimed as the first person to write sheer nonsense for boys and girls, and his poems enjoyed an immediate and enduring popularity. *The butterfly's ball* appeared in the *Gentleman's magazine*, November, 1806. It is presumed that John Harris first saw it there. Numerous editions were published, and a host of imitations sprang into print.

JANE and ANN TAYLOR, 1783-1824 and 1782-1866. Daughters of the Reverend Isaac Taylor of Ongar, a nonconformist minister, who also conducted an engraving business and taught the art to all his children. Both Jane and Ann worked for twelve long hours each day and were skilful engravers. They wrote verses from an early age but their writing was done in the early morning hours or after eight o'clock at night. They began to write plays and verses when they were very young and contributed to an annual, *The minor's pocket book*. The publishers, Darton and Harvey, asked them for more verses which were published as *Original poems for infant minds by several young persons* in 1804. *Select rhymes for the nursery*, published in 1806, was equally popular. Their parents did not encourage their daughters' literary career because they did not approve of female writers, but after their reputation was established both parents began to write books for children themselves. Jane Taylor died in 1824. Her sister, Ann, married the Reverend Joseph Gilbert on Christmas Eve, 1813. She died in 1866 at the age of 84.

SARAH (KIRBY) TRIMMER, 1741-1810. Mrs. Trimmer was the mother of twelve children, a prolific writer, and exponent of the moral tale. She held a place of high esteem in the literary and educational circles of her day.

ELIZABETH TURNER, d. 1846. Lived at Whitchurch, Salop. Hardly anything is known about her.

SAMUEL WILLIAMS, 1788-1853. Of humble birth, Williams was apprenticed to a Colchester printer. He devoted his spare time to drawing and engraving. Settled in London in 1819. He illustrated *The Daisy* and *The Cowslip* by Elizabeth Turner.

Bibliography

ANDREAE, GESIENA. The dawn of juvenile literature in England. Amsterdam, H.J. Paris, 1925.

BARRY, F. V. A century of children's books. London, Methuen & co. Ltd., 1922.

DARTON, F. J. H. Children's books in England. Five centuries of social life. Cambridge, The University Press, 1958. Second edition.

FIELD, MRS. E. M. The child and his book. Some account of the history and progress of children's literature in England. London, Wells Gardner, Darton & co., 1891.

JAMES, PHILIP. Children's books of yesterday. Edited by C. Geoffrey Holme. London, The Studio Ltd.; New York, The Studio Publications, Inc., 1933.

KIEFER, MONICA. American children through their books, 1700-1835. Philadelphia, University of Pennsylvania Press, 1948.

MEIGS, CORNELIA; EATON, ANNE; NESBITT, ELIZABETH, and VIGUERS, RUTH HILL. A critical history of children's literature. A survey of children's books in English, from earliest times to the present, prepared in four parts under the editorship of Cornelia Meigs, New York, The Macmillan Company, 1953.

MUIR, PERCY. English children's books, 1600 to 1900. London, B. T. Batsford Ltd., 1954.

OPIE, IONA and PETER. The Oxford dictionary of nursery rhymes. Oxford, The Clarendon Press, 1951.

ROSENBACH, A. S. W. Early American children's books. Portland, Maine, The Southworth Press, 1953.

THWAITE, M. F. From primer to pleasure. London, Library Association, 1963.

TORONTO PUBLIC LIBRARY. The Osborne Collection of early children's books, 1566-1910; a catalogue, prepared at Boys and Girls House by Judith St. John, with an introduction by Edgar Osborne. Toronto, Canada, Toronto Public Library, 1958.

THE
GOOD CHILD'S
REWARD.

Train up a Child in the way he should go, & when he is old he will not depart from it.